SHURLEY ENGLISH

English Made Easy

This booklet belongs to:

Student Workbook Level 6

04-11
ISBN 978-1-58561-110-2 (Level 6 Student Workbook)

Printed in the United States of America by RR Donnelley, Owensville, MO.

For additional information or to place an order, write to: Shurley Instructional Materials, Inc.
366 SIM Drive
Cabot, AR 72023

1 2 3 4 11 10 09 07

Study Skills Assessment

Directions: Rate your skills in each category by marking the appropriate column with an **X**.

GET ORGANIZED: Reference 2	Excellent	Average	Needs Improvement
1. Being prepared	☐	☐	☐
2. Organizing your desk	☐	☐	☐
3. Putting everything in its place	☐	☐	☐
4. Realizing the importance of directions	☐	☐	☐
5. Proofreading your work	☐	☐	☐

LISTEN: Reference 3	Excellent	Average	Needs Improvement
1. Listening with your whole body	☐	☐	☐
2. Asking questions	☐	☐	☐
3. Taking notes	☐	☐	☐
4. Concentrating	☐	☐	☐
5. Listening to directions	☐	☐	☐

PLAN YOUR TIME: Reference 4	Excellent	Average	Needs Improvement
1. Setting goals for yourself	☐	☐	☐
2. Planning your day	☐	☐	☐
3. Doing what is important first	☐	☐	☐
4. Making each minute count	☐	☐	☐
5. Rewarding yourself	☐	☐	☐

DO YOUR HOMEWORK: Reference 5	Excellent	Average	Needs Improvement
1. Collecting assignments before you leave school	☐	☐	☐
2. Scheduling a time to study	☐	☐	☐
3. Studying where you can concentrate	☐	☐	☐
4. Setting a time limit to study	☐	☐	☐
5. Having a special place to keep homework	☐	☐	☐

If you marked any areas as "Average" or "Needs Improvement," look back at the references in those areas to help you find ways to improve. Find a study-skills partner to check your progress, to encourage you, and to give you advice and help.

Notes:

Classroom Practice 6

Name:____ Date:________________

GRAMMAR

Exercise 1: Fill in the blanks below for this sentence:
That frightened puppy whimpered miserably today.

1. What whimpered miserably today?........... ______________ Subject Noun _____
2. What is being said about puppy?............. _______ _______ Verb _____
3. Whimpered how?.............................. ______________ Adverb _____
4. Whimpered when?............................. ______________ Adverb _____
5. What kind of puppy?.......................... ______________ Adjective _____
6. Which puppy?................................. ______________ Adjective _____
7. Subject Noun, Verb, Pattern 1.................. ______________
8. Skill Check
9. Period, statement, declarative sentence...... ______________
10. Go back to the verb. Divide the complete subject from the complete predicate. _____

Classify this sentence: __________ That frightened puppy whimpered miserably today.

Exercise 2: Name the four parts of speech that you have studied so far.

1.______________ 2.______________ 3.______________ 4.______________

SKILLS

Exercise 3: Put the end mark and the End Mark Flow for each kind of sentence in the blanks. Use these words in your answers: *declarative, exclamatory, imperative, interrogative.*

1. Sit down for dinner__ .... ______________________
2. Did you do well on your exam__ ...... ______________________
3. The fire is out of control__ .... ______________________
4. I'm leaving on my trip tomorrow__.... ______________________

EDITING

Exercise 4: Write the capitalization and punctuation rule numbers for each correction in **bold type**. Use References 11–13 on pages 13–16 to look up the capitalization and punctuation rule numbers.

Will they ever sail the cruise liner**,** **Q**ueen **V**ictoria**,** to **A**ruba**,** **J**amaica**,** and the **B**ahamas**?**

Exercise 5: Put punctuation corrections within the sentence. Write all other corrections above the sentence.
Editing Guide: Capitals: 5 Commas: 3 Misspelled Words: 1 End Marks: 1

dad spent the summar in boulder colorado with his brothers michael and kenneth

Notes:

Classroom Practice 7

Name:______________________________ Date:______________

PRACTICE & REVISED SENTENCES

1. **Write a Practice Sentence according to the labels you choose.**
   Use the SN V labels once. You may use the other labels in any order and as many times as you wish in order to make a Practice Sentence.
   Chapter 2 labels for a Practice Sentence: SN, V, Adj, Adv, A
2. **Write a Revised Sentence. Use the following revision strategies: *synonym (syn), antonym (ant), word change (wc), added word (add), deleted word (delete),* or *no change (nc)*. Under each word, write the abbreviation of the revision strategy you use.**

Labels: ______________________________

Practice: ______________________________

Revised: ______________________________

Strategies: ______________________________

Labels: ______________________________

Practice: ______________________________

Revised: ______________________________

Strategies: ______________________________

Labels: ______________________________

Practice: ______________________________

Revised: ______________________________

Strategies: ______________________________

Notes:

Classroom Practice 8

Name:______________________________ Date:______________

GRAMMAR

▶ **Exercise 1:** Classify each sentence.

1. ________ That small speckled trout swam swiftly away yesterday.

2. ________ The new lawnmower worked extremely well.

3. ________ The extremely exasperated receptionist gazed wistfully outside today.

SKILLS

▶ **Exercise 2:** In each column, cross out the word that does not support the underlined topic at the top.

1. **Amphibians**	2. **Oceans**	3. **Planets**
frogs	Atlantic	Mars
jellyfish	Pacific	Earth
toads	Arctic	Peter
salamanders	Vermont	Venus
newts	Indian	Jupiter

▶ **Exercise 3:** Write the name of the topic that best describes what each column of words is about. Choose from these topics. **Weather Cities Electronics Seasons Gases Holidays**

1. ________	2. ________	3. ________
Independence Day	stereo	carbon monoxide
New Year's Day	computer	helium
Presidents' Day	calculator	hydrogen
Armistice Day	television	oxygen

▶ **Exercise 4:** Cross out the sentence in each paragraph that does not support the topic.

Topic: A Hurricane

Store windows are boarded up before the mighty storm. Tall waves rush onto the coastline. Strong winds batter buildings. The ground shakes and splits. .

Topic: Underwater

Deep in the ocean, thousands of creatures move freely. Seals bask in the sun on the shore. Sea turtles glide between strands of algae. Starfish and sand dollars litter the ocean floor.

EDITING

▶ **Exercise 5:** Put punctuation corrections within the sentence. Write all other corrections above the sentence.
Editing Guide: Capitals: 8 Commas: 2 Quotations: 2 Periods: 3 Misspelled Words: 1 End Marks: 1

mr j c brewer sang the song america in the talent contest at webster elementery school

Notes:

Chapter 2 Checkup 9

Name:______________________________ Date:______________

GRAMMAR

Exercise 1: Classify each sentence.

1. __________ The three incredibly tired little boys fell asleep instantly.

2. __________ An enraged black hornet buzzed very angrily nearby!

3. __________ Several large Canadian geese flew high overhead.

Exercise 2: Name the four parts of speech that you have studied so far.

1.______________ 2.______________ 3.______________ 4.______________

SKILLS

Exercise 3: Read the topic and paragraph. Cross out the sentence that does not support the topic.

Topic: **Saturn**

Saturn's pale butterscotch-colored surface and its huge halo of rings make it a planet of beauty. Its color is caused by ammonia gases, and its huge rings surround the planet. Saturn's rings are made of billions of chips of ice and dust that are the size of ice cubes. Uranus also has rings, but they are much smaller. Saturn has a very windy surface and more moons than any other planet.

Exercise 4: Put the end mark and the End Mark Flow for each kind of sentence in the blanks. Use these words in your answers: *declarative, exclamatory, imperative, interrogative.*

1. Erase the chalkboard___ .... ______________________________
2. Did you wash the car___............... ______________________________
3. A spider is in my soup___ .... ______________________________
4. I skated across the frozen pond___ ... ______________________________

EDITING

Exercise 5: Write the capitalization and punctuation rule numbers for each correction in **bold type**. Use References 11–13 on pages 13–16 to look up the capitalization and punctuation rule numbers.

Sandra**,** will you work in the nursery on **S**unday**,** **A**pril 18**?**

Exercise 6: Put punctuation corrections within the sentence. Write all other corrections above the sentence.
Editing Guide: Capitals: 3 Commas: 2 Misspelled Words: 2 End Marks: 1

my sister and i like to eat turkey sweet potatos and pumkin pie on thanksgiving

Notes:

Prewriting Map

Name:______________________________ Date:______________

Purpose: ______________________________

Type of Writing: ______________________________

Audience: ______________________________

Topic: ______________________________

TOPIC

1ST MAIN POINT

SUPPORTING DETAIL

SUPPORTING DETAIL

SUPPORTING DETAIL

2ND MAIN POINT

SUPPORTING DETAIL

SUPPORTING DETAIL

SUPPORTING DETAIL

3RD MAIN POINT

SUPPORTING DETAIL

SUPPORTING DETAIL

SUPPORTING DETAIL

Notes:

Sentence Outline for an Expository Paragraph

Name:______________________________ Date:______________

Purpose: ______________________________

Type of Writing: ______________________________

Audience: ______________________________

Topic: ______________________________

List 3 points about the topic:

1.______________ 2.______________ 3.______________

Sentence 1 — Write a topic and number sentence.

____

____

Sentence 2 — Write a three-point sentence.

____

____

Sentence 3 — State your first point in a complete sentence.

____

Sentence 4 — Write a supporting sentence for the first point.

____

____

Sentence 5 — State your second point in a complete sentence.

____

Sentence 6 — Write a supporting sentence for the second point.

____

____

Sentence 7 — State your third point in a complete sentence.

____

Sentence 8 — Write a supporting sentence for the third point.

____

____

Sentence 9 — Write a concluding general sentence.

____

____

Notes:

Chapter 2 Writing Evaluation Guide

Name:______________________________ Date:______________

ROUGH DRAFT CHECK

_____ 1. Did you write your rough draft in pencil?
_____ 2. Did you write the correct headings on the first seven lines of your paper?
_____ 3. Did you use extra wide margins and skip every other line?
_____ 4. Did you write a title at the end of your rough draft?
_____ 5. Did you place your edited rough draft in your Rough Draft folder?

REVISING CHECK

_____ 6. Did you identify the purpose, type of writing, and audience?
_____ 7. Did you check for a topic, topic sentence, and sentences supporting the topic?
_____ 8. Did you check sentences for the right order, and did you combine, rearrange, or delete sentences when necessary?
_____ 9. Did you check for a variety of simple, compound, and complex sentences?
_____ 10. Did you check for any left out, repeated, or unnecessary words?
_____ 11. Did you check for the best choice of words by replacing or deleting unclear words?
_____ 12. Did you check the content for interest and creativity?
_____ 13. Did you check the voice to make sure the writing says what you want it to say?

EDITING CHECK

_____ 14. Did you indent each paragraph?
_____ 15. Did you put an end mark at the end of every sentence?
_____ 16. Did you capitalize the first word of every sentence?
_____ 17. Did you check for all other capitalization mistakes?
_____ 18. Did you check for all punctuation mistakes? *(commas, periods, apostrophes, quotation marks, underlining)*
_____ 19. Did you check for misspelled words and for incorrect homonym choices?
_____ 20. Did you check for incorrect spellings of plural and possessive forms?
_____ 21. Did you check for correct construction and punctuation of your sentences?
_____ 22. Did you check for usage mistakes? *(subject/verb agreement, a/an choices, contractions, verb tenses, pronoun/antecedent agreement, pronoun cases, degrees of adjectives, double negatives, etc.)*
_____ 23. Did you put your revised and edited paper in the Rough Draft folder?

FINAL PAPER CHECK

_____ 24. Did you write the final paper in pencil?
_____ 25. Did you center the title on the top line and center your name under the title?
_____ 26. Did you skip a line before starting the writing assignment?
_____ 27. Did you single-space, use wide margins, and write the final paper neatly?
_____ 28. Did you staple your papers in this order: final paper on top, rough draft in the middle, and prewriting map on the bottom? Did you put them in the Final Paper folder?

Notes:

Classroom Practice 10

Name:______________________________ Date:______________

GRAMMAR

▶ **Exercise 1:** Classify each sentence. Underline the complete subject once and the complete predicate twice.

1. __________ Several ripe red apples fell from the tree in the backyard.

2. __________ Ms. Johnson waited patiently in the long line of traffic on the highway.

▶ **Exercise 2:** Use Sentence 2 above to complete the table below.

List the Noun Used	List the Noun Job	Singular or Plural	Common or Proper	Simple Subject	Simple Predicate

▶ **Exercise 3:** Name the five parts of speech that you have studied so far.

1. __________ 2. __________ 3. __________ 4. __________ 5. __________

▶ **Exercise 4:** Underline the complete subject once and the complete predicate twice.

1. The dangerous lion growled menacingly!
2. Ten black motorcycles raced away.
3. Several large Canadian geese honked loudly.
4. The political candidates argued heatedly.

▶ **Exercise 5:** Underline the simple subject once and the simple predicate twice.

1. A small mouse dashed across the room!
2. A few rude students talked continuously.
3. The nine orange balloons drifted across the sky.
4. The champion skater performed for the crowd.

SKILLS

▶ **Exercise 6:** Write **S** for singular or **P** for plural.

Noun	S or P
1. shepherd	__________
2. robots	__________
3. shoulder	__________
4. foreigners	__________

▶ **Exercise 7:** Write **C** for common or **P** for proper.

Noun	C or P
1. ostrich	__________
2. Smoky Mountains	__________
3. Albuquerque	__________
4. planetarium	__________

EDITING

▶ **Exercise 8:** Put punctuation corrections within the sentence. Write all other corrections above the sentence.
Editing Guide: Capitals: 7 Commas: 2 Periods: 1 End Marks: 1

james g jones the president of the valley rotary club gave dad an award for his excellent service

Notes:

Classroom Practice 11

Name:______________________________ Date:____________

GRAMMAR

Exercise 1: Classify each sentence. Underline the complete subject once and the complete predicate twice.

1.__________ The column of smoke rose high into the morning air.

2.__________ Leah walked up the steep steps to a seat in the bleachers.

3.__________ The cool water flowed openly from the mouth of the cave.

Exercise 2: Use Sentence 1 above to complete the table below.

List the Noun Used	List the Noun Job	Singular or Plural	Common or Proper	Simple Subject	Simple Predicate

SKILLS

Exercise 3: For each sentence, do three things: (1) Write the subject. (2) Write **S** and **Rule 1** if the subject is singular, or write **P** and **Rule 2** if the subject is plural. (3) Underline the correct verb.

Rule 1: A singular subject must use a singular verb form that ends in **s** or **es**.
Rule 2: A plural subject, a compound subject, or the subject **YOU** must use a plural verb form that has **no s** or **es** endings. (A plural verb form is also called the *plain form*.)

Subject	S or P	Rule	
			1. The gopher (dig, digs) in the flowerbed.
			2. You (chew, chews) with your mouth closed.
			3. Lynn and Rose (was, were) studying diligently.
			4. The turkey (is, are) in the oven.
			5. Alex and Alicia (is, are) going to the game.
			6. The dog (need, needs) a bath before dark.
			7. The new lawnmower (do, does) a great job.
			8. The boys (wasn't, weren't) here today, Derrick.
			9. Your lotion (help, helps) my chapped hands.
			10. We (was, were) hunting yesterday.

EDITING

Exercise 4: Put punctuation corrections within the sentence. Write all other corrections above the sentence.
Editing Guide: Capitals: 9 Commas: 4 Subject-Verb Agreement: 1 Misspelled words: 1 End Marks: 1

my three freinds nick trey and travis visits the statue of liberty on their tour of new york city today

Notes:

Classroom Practice 12

Name:______________________________ Date:______________

GRAMMAR

▶ **Exercise 1:** Classify each sentence. Underline the complete subject once and the complete predicate twice.

1. __________ The small goldfish swam swiftly toward the large body of water.

2. __________ The motor of the large model airplane worked extremely well during the tryouts.

▶ **Exercise 2:** Use Sentence 2 above to complete the table below.

List the Noun Used	List the Noun Job	Singular or Plural	Common or Proper	Simple Subject	Simple Predicate

SKILLS

▶ **Exercise 3:** Underline the correct homonym in each sentence.

1. The baby seal swam to (its, it's) mother.
2. I want cake for my last (coarse, course).
3. He (led, lead) his team to victory.
4. Chess is his (principal, principle) interest.
5. Our population is (stationery, stationary).
6. The tree put (forth, fourth) large green leaves.
7. (There, Their, They're) going to the office.
8. (Its, It's) a very hot day outside.

▶ **Exercise 4:** For each sentence, do three things: (1) Write the subject. (2) Write **S** and **Rule 1** if the subject is singular, or write **P** and **Rule 2** if the subject is plural. (3) Underline the correct verb.

Subject	S or P	Rule	
			1. The mailman (deliver, delivers) the mail on time.
			2. Cats and dogs (is, are) natural enemies.
			3. You (drive, drives) to the game tonight.
			4. Those two men (has, have) the same sunglasses.
			5. The satellite slowly (circle, circles) the Earth.
			6. You (turn, turns) your assignment in over there.
			7. The woman in the store (give, gives) good directions.
			8. Several boys (was, were) late for class.
			9. An otter (play, plays) happily in the water.

EDITING

▶ **Exercise 5:** Correct each mistake. **Editing Guide: End Marks: 4 Capitals: 11 Commas: 3 Homonyms: 5 Subject-Verb Agreement: 2 Periods: 2 Misspelled Words: 3**

our neighbors mr and mrs bonelli has an italian resturant inn madison wisconsin

my hole family love too eat their we go every saterday knight it is delisious

Notes:

Chapter 3 Checkup 13

Name:______________________________ Date:______________

GRAMMAR

Exercise 1: Classify each sentence. Underline the complete subject once and the complete predicate twice.

1. __________ Sarah drove too fast for safety on the icy roads during rush-hour traffic.

2. __________ A large, colorful peacock strutted confidently along the edge of the water.

3. __________ The extremely talented cast of actors performed especially well tonight.

Exercise 2: Use Sentence 1 above to complete the table below.

List the Noun Used	List the Noun Job	Singular or Plural	Common or Proper	Simple Subject	Simple Predicate

SKILLS

Exercise 3: For each sentence, do three things: (1) Write the subject. (2) Write **S** and **Rule 1** if the subject is singular, or write **P** and **Rule 2** if the subject is plural. (3) Underline the correct verb.

Subject	S or P	Rule	
______	______	______	1. You (pick, picks) your own topic for this assignment.
______	______	______	2. The rooster (crows, crow) every morning.
______	______	______	3. Glenn and Colleen (is, are) my new neighbors.
______	______	______	4. Your articles (wasn't, weren't) in last week's paper.

EDITING

Exercise 4: Correct each mistake. **Editing Guide: End Marks: 6 Capitals: 13 Commas: 3 Homonyms: 2 Subject-Verb Agreement: 2 Misspelled Words: 3**

lewis martinez my cousin pulled a muscle inn his write arm at the weight-lifting competiton on thrsday in boise idaho he still placed second we was so proud of him mama even hugged him papa and uncle ernest was taking rolls of film of lewis we had a fantasic time

Notes:

Classroom Practice 14

Name:______________________________ Date:______________

INDEPENDENT PRACTICE & REVISED SENTENCES

1. Write a Practice Sentence according to the labels you choose.
   Use the SN V labels once. You may use the other labels in any order and as many times as you wish in order to make a Practice Sentence.
   Chapter 3 labels for a Practice Sentence: SN, V, Adj, Adv, A, P, OP
2. Write a Revised Sentence. Use the following revision strategies: *synonym (syn), antonym (ant), word change (wc), added word (add), deleted word (delete),* or *no change (nc)*. Under each word, write the abbreviation of the revision strategy you use.

Labels: ______________________________

Practice: ______________________________

Revised: ______________________________

Strategies: ______________________________

Labels: ______________________________

Practice: ______________________________

Revised: ______________________________

Strategies: ______________________________

Labels: ______________________________

Practice: ______________________________

Revised: ______________________________

Strategies: ______________________________

Notes:

Chapter 3 Writing Evaluation Guide

Name:_______________________________ Date:_______________

ROUGH DRAFT CHECK

_______ 1. Did you write your rough draft in pencil?
_______ 2. Did you write the correct headings on the first seven lines of your paper?
_______ 3. Did you use extra wide margins and skip every other line?
_______ 4. Did you write a title at the end of your rough draft?
_______ 5. Did you place your edited rough draft in your Rough Draft folder?

REVISING CHECK

_______ 6. Did you identify the purpose, type of writing, and audience?
_______ 7. Did you check for a topic, topic sentence, and sentences supporting the topic?
_______ 8. Did you check sentences for the right order, and did you combine, rearrange, or delete sentences when necessary?
_______ 9. Did you check for a variety of simple, compound, and complex sentences?
_______ 10. Did you check for any left out, repeated, or unnecessary words?
_______ 11. Did you check for the best choice of words by replacing or deleting unclear words?
_______ 12. Did you check the content for interest and creativity?
_______ 13. Did you check the voice to make sure the writing says what you want it to say?

EDITING CHECK

_______ 14. Did you indent each paragraph?
_______ 15. Did you put an end mark at the end of every sentence?
_______ 16. Did you capitalize the first word of every sentence?
_______ 17. Did you check for all other capitalization mistakes?
_______ 18. Did you check for all punctuation mistakes? *(commas, periods, apostrophes, quotation marks, underlining)*
_______ 19. Did you check for misspelled words and for incorrect homonym choices?
_______ 20. Did you check for incorrect spellings of plural and possessive forms?
_______ 21. Did you check for correct construction and punctuation of your sentences?
_______ 22. Did you check for usage mistakes? *(subject/verb agreement, a/an choices, contractions, verb tenses, pronoun/antecedent agreement, pronoun cases, degrees of adjectives, double negatives, etc.)*
_______ 23. Did you put your revised and edited paper in the Rough Draft folder?

FINAL PAPER CHECK

_______ 24. Did you write the final paper in pencil?
_______ 25. Did you center the title on the top line and center your name under the title?
_______ 26. Did you skip a line before starting the writing assignment?
_______ 27. Did you single-space, use wide margins, and write the final paper neatly?
_______ 28. Did you staple your papers in this order: final paper on top, rough draft in the middle, and prewriting map on the bottom? Did you put them in the Final Paper folder?

Notes:

Classroom Practice 15

Name:______________________________ Date:______________

GRAMMAR

▶ **Exercise 1:** Classify each sentence. Underline the complete subject once and the complete predicate twice.

1. __________ Study for your French test with Patrick and Susan after school today.

2. __________ Larry and I worked on my research report yesterday.

SKILLS

▶ **Exercise 2:** Identify each type of sentence by writing the correct label in the blank. (**Labels: S, F, SCS, SCV**)

__________ 1. He and she rode to town with me.
__________ 2. After the students sat down.
__________ 3. Tiny gnats flew around my face and annoyed me.
__________ 4. Peanuts and pecans make good snacks.
__________ 5. Climb to the top of the tower and look over the city at night.
__________ 6. The old fox walked wearily down the dark road in search of easy food.
__________ 7. My brother's package arrived late and did not have a return address.
__________ 8. After the pie was eaten.
__________ 9. The flour, sugar, and milk for the recipe are on the counter.

▶ **Exercise 3:** Use a slash to separate the two complete thoughts in each run-on sentence. Correct the run-on sentences as indicated by the labels in parentheses at the end of each sentence.

1. The farmer plowed the fields the farmer planted his crops. **(SCV)**
____
2. My mother cooked our family a Thanksgiving meal my sister helped Mother cook. **(SCS)**
____
3. The leftover roast is in the refrigerator the left-over apple pie is in the refrigerator. **(SCS)**
____
4. Grandfather jumped up he walked quickly to the door. **(SCV)**
____

EDITING

▶ **Exercise 4:** Correct each mistake. **Editing Guide: End Marks: 3 Capitals: 8 Commas: 2 Homonyms: 7 Periods: 1 Underlining: 1 Misspelled Words: 1**

did you reed white fang a classick bye jack london in you're forth-grade class last year i red it and made a book report on it mrs smith had us reed a knew book this year

Notes:

Classroom Practice 16

Name:______________________________ Date:______________

GRAMMAR

▶ **Exercise 1:** Classify each sentence. Underline the complete subject once and the complete predicate twice.

1. __________ Talk to my parents about my permission slip and my ticket for the concert.

2. __________ Tom and Kay worked hard for their college degrees from our local college.

SKILLS

▶ **Exercise 2:** Write either the contraction or the contraction words in the blanks.

1. do not __________ 2. let's __________ 3. does not __________ 4. I've __________

▶ **Exercise 3:** Write **a** or **an** in the blanks.

1. We found _____ ant and _____ beetle. 2. I ate _____ cherry tart and _____ apple pie at the picnic.

▶ **Exercise 4:** Identify each type of sentence by writing the correct label in the blank. (**Labels: S, F, SCS, SCV**)

__________ 1. Cheetahs and zebras are my favorite animals.
__________ 2. Our neighbor's dog chewed the paper and scattered it around the yard.
__________ 3. As soon as the director raised his hands.
__________ 4. Jarrod's more experienced crew built the house in record time.
__________ 5. Mrs. Garner graded our papers and put them in our folders.
__________ 6. The two girls and their friends shopped at the mall.
__________ 7. Derek and I rode to town with Mr. Poole after school.
__________ 8. The mail carrier did not deliver Dad's overnight package to our house today.

▶ **Exercise 5:** Use a slash to separate the two complete thoughts in each run-on sentence.
Correct the run-on sentences as indicated by the labels in parentheses at the end of each sentence.

1. The students were yawning they were bored. (**S, S**)
____
2. The seamstress worked at home her husband worked at home. (**SCS**)
____
3. The audience stood up they cheered for the cast. (**SCV**)
____

EDITING

▶ **Exercise 6:** Correct each mistake. **Editing Guide: End Marks: 6 Capitals: 12 Commas: 2 Apostrophes: 1 Homonyms: 5 A/An: 2 Subject-Verb Agreement: 4 Periods: 1 Misspelled Words: 2**

patty and i sea mr perry hour sixth-grade english techer at meadowlark mall in an baby store we giggel at the look on his face and walks over he tell us that he are buying an baby gift for his wife we lead him too the write area and then says farewell we look back hes still standing their

Notes:

Classroom Practice 17

Name:______________________________ Date:______________

GRAMMAR

▶ **Exercise 1:** Classify each sentence. Underline the complete subject once and the complete predicate twice.

1. __________ The frightened little girl and her mother called frantically to the firemen!

2. __________ Look at this gorgeous view and beautiful sunset in the Grand Canyon!

SKILLS

▶ **Exercise 2:** Write **a** or **an** in the blanks.

I ate _____ banana and _____ orange for dessert.

▶ **Exercise 3:** Write the contraction in the blank.

1. did not __________ 2. I am __________

▶ **Exercise 4:** Identify each type of sentence by writing the correct label in the blank. (**Labels: S, F, SCS, SCV**)

__________ 1. Chase and Cooper invited me to dinner.
__________ 2. Shady and cool spot on the lawn.
__________ 3. We watched a scary movie last night and were not able to sleep.
__________ 4. After school on Friday, you and I are going out for dinner.
__________ 5. Celia grabbed her book bag and dashed out the door.
__________ 6. During the half-time show at the ballgame on Saturday night.
__________ 7. The icicle melted slowly and dripped steadily throughout the day.

▶ **Exercise 5:** Use a slash to separate the two complete thoughts in each run-on sentence. Correct the run-on sentences as indicated by the labels in parentheses at the end of each sentence.

1. The baby kangaroos hopped around they chewed on tender leaves. (**SCV**)

____

2. Tate mowed the grass Charlie mowed with him. (**SCS**)

____

3. The hard rain drenched the backyard it also drowned the flowers. (**SCV**)

____

EDITING

▶ **Exercise 6:** Correct each mistake. **Editing Guide: End Marks: 2 Capitals: 15 Commas: 2 Homonyms: 2 Subject-Verb Agreement: 3 Underlining: 1 Misspelled Words: 2**

in my favorite book where the red fern grows billy and his courageous pups lives and grows up in the ozark mountains and has many adventures i bought many copies of this book fore memers of the walker middle school student council too sell for our fund-raiser in septemer

Notes:

Chapter 4 Checkup 18

Name:______________________________________ Date:______________

GRAMMAR

▶ **Exercise 1:** Classify each sentence. Underline the complete subject once and the complete predicate twice.

1. __________ Go quickly to the hardware store for plumbing putty and three copper pipes.

2. __________ Hannah and Sarina waved to their friends from the top of the escalator.

3. __________ The smell of the hot cinnamon rolls drifted from our sidewalk café yesterday.

SKILLS

▶ **Exercise 2:** Write **a** or **an** in the blanks.

I like _____ onion with _____ grilled steak.

▶ **Exercise 3:** Write the contraction in the blank.

1. they have __________ 2. are not __________

▶ **Exercise 4:** Identify each type of sentence by writing the correct label in the blank. (**Labels: S, F, SCS, SCV**)

__________ 1. Barely missed the car's fender.
__________ 2. During the evenings, my parents would take long walks along the beach.
__________ 3. Our uncle made puppets and sold them at the fair.
__________ 4. She and I ran to my neighbor's house down the street.
__________ 5. Larry and the neighborhood boys loaded up the camping equipment.
__________ 6. We clapped our hands and danced to the rhythm of the music.

▶ **Exercise 5:** Use a slash to separate the two complete thoughts in each run-on sentence.
Correct the run-on sentences as indicated by the labels in parentheses at the end of each sentence.

1. My sister cleaned her room today my brother cleaned his room today. (**SCS**)

____

2. My dad cooked the pizza he also cleaned the kitchen. (**SCV**)

____

3. The student raised his hand he waited patiently for permission to speak. (**SCV**)

____

EDITING

▶ **Exercise 6:** Correct each mistake. **Editing Guide: End Marks: 7 Capitals: 13 Apostrophes: 2 Homonyms: 2 A/An: 1 Subject-Verb Agreement: 5 Misspelled Words: 2**

the stormy weather makes kevins homework even harder too do he sit at the computer and stare at the blank screen his expostory essay on the french revolution are due on thersday in world history ll he tap lightly on the keys and tries to think where he should begin a unexpected surge of electricity leave the computer screen blank kevin chuckles too himself he is suddenly very glad he hasnt written his essay

Notes:

Classroom Practice 19

Name:________________________________ Date:____________

INDEPENDENT PRACTICE & REVISED SENTENCES

1. **Write a Practice Sentence according to the labels you choose.**
   Use SN/SP V as your main labels. You may use the other labels in any order and as many times as you wish in order to make a Practice Sentence.
   Chapter 4 labels for a Practice Sentence: SN/SP, V, Adj, Adv, A, P, OP, PPA, C
2. **Write a Revised Sentence. Use the following revision strategies: *synonym (syn), antonym (ant), word change (wc), added word (add), deleted word (delete),* or *no change (nc)*. Under each word, write the abbreviation of the revision strategy you use.**

Labels: ____

Practice: ____

Revised: ____

Strategies: ____

Labels: ____

Practice: ____

Revised: ____

Strategies: ____

Labels: ____

Practice: ____

Revised: ____

Strategies: ____

Notes:

Chapter 4 Writing Evaluation Guide

Name:______________________________ Date:______________

ROUGH DRAFT CHECK

_____ 1. Did you write your rough draft in pencil?
_____ 2. Did you write the correct headings on the first seven lines of your paper?
_____ 3. Did you use extra wide margins and skip every other line?
_____ 4. Did you write a title at the end of your rough draft?
_____ 5. Did you place your edited rough draft in your Rough Draft folder?

REVISING CHECK

_____ 6. Did you identify the purpose, type of writing, and audience?
_____ 7. Did you check for a topic, topic sentence, and sentences supporting the topic?
_____ 8. Did you check sentences for the right order, and did you combine, rearrange, or delete sentences when necessary?
_____ 9. Did you check for a variety of simple, compound, and complex sentences?
_____ 10. Did you check for any left out, repeated, or unnecessary words?
_____ 11. Did you check for the best choice of words by replacing or deleting unclear words?
_____ 12. Did you check the content for interest and creativity?
_____ 13. Did you check the voice to make sure the writing says what you want it to say?

EDITING CHECK

_____ 14. Did you indent each paragraph?
_____ 15. Did you put an end mark at the end of every sentence?
_____ 16. Did you capitalize the first word of every sentence?
_____ 17. Did you check for all other capitalization mistakes?
_____ 18. Did you check for all punctuation mistakes? *(commas, periods, apostrophes, quotation marks, underlining)*
_____ 19. Did you check for misspelled words and for incorrect homonym choices?
_____ 20. Did you check for incorrect spellings of plural and possessive forms?
_____ 21. Did you check for correct construction and punctuation of your sentences?
_____ 22. Did you check for usage mistakes? *(subject/verb agreement, a/an choices, contractions, verb tenses, pronoun/antecedent agreement, pronoun cases, degrees of adjectives, double negatives, etc.)*
_____ 23. Did you put your revised and edited paper in the Rough Draft folder?

FINAL PAPER CHECK

_____ 24. Did you write the final paper in pencil?
_____ 25. Did you center the title on the top line and center your name under the title?
_____ 26. Did you skip a line before starting the writing assignment?
_____ 27. Did you single-space, use wide margins, and write the final paper neatly?
_____ 28. Did you staple your papers in this order: final paper on top, rough draft in the middle, and prewriting map on the bottom? Did you put them in the Final Paper folder?

Notes:

Classroom Practice 20

Name:______________________________ Date:______________

GRAMMAR

▶ **Exercise 1:** Classify each sentence.

1. __________ Yesterday, Eddie and his brother did not arrive at the coliseum in time for the concert.

2. __________ A huge riot suddenly erupted in the city streets of Italy after the chaotic soccer match!

SKILLS

▶ **Exercise 2:** Identify each type of sentence by writing the correct label in the blank. (**Labels: S, F, SCS, SCV, CD**)

__________ 1. Scrubbing the hideous stain on the floor.
__________ 2. The scent of fresh fudge filled the air, and it was mouthwatering.
__________ 3. The leaves and stems were wilted from the intense heat.
__________ 4. Emma dribbled around the guard and shot the ball.
__________ 5. It was cold outside; I wore my heavy coat.
__________ 6. The waitress brought our food orders and refilled our drinks.
__________ 7. Darren kicked the football, but he missed the field goal.
__________ 8. The team was finally defeated; therefore, they were no longer the champions.
__________ 9. Pine cones and acorns littered our front yard.

▶ **Exercise 3:** Use a slash to separate each run-on sentence below. Then, correct the run-on sentences by rewriting them as indicated by the labels in parentheses at the end of each sentence.

1. The sky was cloudy it did not rain. (**CD; however,**)

____

2. The competition was fierce everyone kept a positive attitude. (**CD, yet**)

____

3. Jackson and Mariana are leaving before noon I am leaving with them. (**SCS**)

____

4. The lecture was long I took detailed notes until the end. (**CD, but**)

____

5. Reggie washed his car Saturday afternoon he also waxed it. (**SCV**)

____

EDITING

▶ **Exercise 4:** Correct each mistake. **Editing Guide: End Marks: 6 Capitals: 6 Commas: 4 Apostrophes: 1 Homonyms: 4 A/An: 2 Subject-Verb Agreement: 5 Misspelled Words: 1**

judy digs threw her purse in an panic but she cant find her keys she look in the car and in the driveway but her keys are not their judy is getting hot so she take off her coat suddenly she hear her keys rattling in her coat pocket they has been there the hole time she breathes an sigh of releaf and head happily two her car

Notes:

Classroom Practice 21

Name:______________________________ Date:______________

GRAMMAR

▶ **Exercise 1:** Classify each sentence.

1. __________ Did Eddie and Bo travel to the East by train for their vacation?

2. __________ Yesterday, the pilot of the huge jet finally landed safely with two damaged engines!

SKILLS

▶ **Exercise 2:** Identify each type of sentence by writing the correct label in the blank. (**Labels: S, F, SCS, SCV, CD**)

__________ 1. The tiny feather drifted slowly and landed on the ground.
__________ 2. Dad watched television; Mom read a book.
__________ 3. Our dog and cat pawed at the back door.
__________ 4. Crammed into the crowded elevator.
__________ 5. Anne vacuumed the carpet, and Lydia dusted the furniture.

▶ **Exercise 3:** Use a slash to separate each run-on sentence below. Then, correct the run-on sentences by rewriting them as indicated by the labels in parentheses at the end of each sentence.

1. The eager boy fished with his father they caught no fish. (**CD, but**)

____

2. The eager boy fished with his father they caught no fish. (**CD; however,**)

____

3. The eager boy talked with his father he fished with his father. (**SCV**)

____

4. The eager boy fished with his father they caught no fish. (**CD;**)

____

5. The boy was fishing with his father the girl was fishing with her father. (**SCS**)

____

EDITING

▶ **Exercise 4:** Correct each mistake. **Editing Guide: End Marks: 5 Capitals: 5 Commas: 2 Homonyms: 2 A/An: 1 Subject-Verb Agreement: 6 Misspelled Words: 1**

jill suddenly hear a unhappy howl she look out the window and see her hunting dog all tangled up again his chain is in one huge not and he cannot reach his water he are looking toward the door with sorowful eyes jill untangle him and he lick her hand and wags his tale

Notes:

Classroom Practice 22

Name:______________________________ Date:______________

GRAMMAR

Exercise 1: Classify each sentence.

1. __________ At noon, the signal light at the intersection was not working.

2. __________ Melinda and Marie sing beautifully with the grace and style of concert performers.

Exercise 2: List the seven parts of speech you have studied so far.

1. __________ 2.__________ 3.__________ 4.__________ 5.__________ 6.__________ 7.__________

SKILLS

Exercise 3: Identify each type of sentence by writing the correct label in the blank. (**Labels: S, F, SCS, SCV, CD**)

__________ 1. Our knives and forks are packed away.
__________ 2. Had long, curly hair with a red bow to match her red dress.
__________ 3. Claire poured the milk in a large glass, and Lori drank it.
__________ 4. My brothers went to the library but did not get any books.
__________ 5. The homework was hard; however, I did it.

Exercise 4: Use a slash to separate each run-on sentence below. Then, correct the run-on sentences by rewriting them as indicated by the labels in parentheses at the end of each sentence.

1. You must answer the phone you will miss your call. (**CD; otherwise,**)
____
2. You must answer the phone you will miss your call. (**CD, or**)
____
3. Answer the phone take a message. (**SCV**)
____
4. Carla will answer the phone Amelia will answer the phone. (**SCS**)
____
5. The mountain climber struggled he made it to the top. (**CD, but**)
____
6. Kerri is at band practice until 6:00 Terri is at band practice until 6:00. (**SCS**)
____

EDITING

Exercise 5: Correct each mistake. **Editing Guide: End Marks: 4 Capitals: 10 Commas: 3 Homonyms: 3 Subject-Verb Agreement: 1 Misspelled Words: 2**

i made eggs and biscuits four jermaine and reggie this morning they was tasty in fact jermaine ate fore eggs and reggie ate to after breckfast the boys left for school at dover collage

Notes:

Chapter 5 Checkup 23

Name:_______________________________________ Date:_______________

GRAMMAR

Exercise 1: Classify each sentence.

1. __________ The skydiver did not hesitate for a second during his first jump!

2. __________ During the summer, Joan and Dana frequently jogged around the track.

3. __________ Will you come to the school play with Sam and me on Saturday?

SKILLS

Exercise 2: Identify each type of sentence by writing the correct label in the blank. (**Labels: S, F, SCS, SCV, CD**)

__________ 1. The Halloween candy on sale in the stores.
__________ 2. I jog in the mornings; my sister jogs in the evenings.
__________ 3. We yelled and cheered with the cheerleaders throughout the game.
__________ 4. My alarm did not go off; otherwise, I would have been on time.
__________ 5. Waves crashed against the rocks and rolled back out to sea.
__________ 6. We play in the sand along the beach near our home.
__________ 7. The rooster and two hens pecked for insects in the yard.
__________ 8. Sam must finish his chores, or he cannot go to the movie tonight.

Exercise 3: Use a slash to separate each run-on sentence below. Then, correct the run-on sentences by rewriting them as indicated by the labels in parentheses at the end of each sentence.

1. The artist painted a picture he cleaned his brushes. (**CD, and**)

____

2. The artist painted several pictures his student painted several pictures. (**SCS**)

____

3. The artist painted a picture he cleaned his brushes. (**SCV**)

____

4. The students had much work to do they went to recess. (**CD; however,**)

____

5. The newborn colt struggled to his feet he was still wobbly. (**CD, but**)

____

EDITING

Exercise 4: Correct each mistake. **Editing Guide: End Marks: 3 Capitals: 11 Commas: 1 Homonyms: 4 Subject-Verb Agreement: 2 Misspelled Words: 1**

doug and i arrives on a plain from houston inn time four the annual maple syrup festival in rutland vermont the hoie town turns out for this delishous celebration doug and i loves the food

Notes:

Classroom Practice 24

INDEPENDENT PRACTICE & REVISED SENTENCES

1. Write a Practice Sentence according to the labels you choose.
   Use **SN/SP V** as your main labels. You may use the other labels in any order and as many times as you wish in order to make a Practice Sentence.
   Chapter 5 labels for a Practice Sentence: SN/SP, V, Adj, Adv, A, P, OP, PPA, C, HV
2. Write a Revised Sentence. Use the following revision strategies: ***synonym (syn), antonym (ant), word change (wc), added word (add), deleted word (delete)***, or ***no change (nc)***. Under each word, write the abbreviation of the revision strategy you use.

Labels: ______________________________

Practice: ______________________________

Revised: ______________________________

Strategies: ______________________________

Labels: ______________________________

Practice: ______________________________

Revised: ______________________________

Strategies: ______________________________

Labels: ______________________________

Practice: ______________________________

Revised: ______________________________

Strategies: ______________________________

Notes:

Chapter 5 Writing Evaluation Guide

Name:______________________________ Date:______________

ROUGH DRAFT CHECK

_______ 1. Did you write your rough draft in pencil?
_______ 2. Did you write the correct headings on the first seven lines of your paper?
_______ 3. Did you use extra wide margins and skip every other line?
_______ 4. Did you write a title at the end of your rough draft?
_______ 5. Did you place your edited rough draft in your Rough Draft folder?

REVISING CHECK

_______ 6. Did you identify the purpose, type of writing, and audience?
_______ 7. Did you check for a topic, topic sentence, and sentences supporting the topic?
_______ 8. Did you check sentences for the right order, and did you combine, rearrange, or delete sentences when necessary?
_______ 9. Did you check for a variety of simple, compound, and complex sentences?
_______ 10. Did you check for any left out, repeated, or unnecessary words?
_______ 11. Did you check for the best choice of words by replacing or deleting unclear words?
_______ 12. Did you check the content for interest and creativity?
_______ 13. Did you check the voice to make sure the writing says what you want it to say?

EDITING CHECK

_______ 14. Did you indent each paragraph?
_______ 15. Did you put an end mark at the end of every sentence?
_______ 16. Did you capitalize the first word of every sentence?
_______ 17. Did you check for all other capitalization mistakes?
_______ 18. Did you check for all punctuation mistakes? *(commas, periods, apostrophes, quotation marks, underlining)*
_______ 19. Did you check for misspelled words and for incorrect homonym choices?
_______ 20. Did you check for incorrect spellings of plural and possessive forms?
_______ 21. Did you check for correct construction and punctuation of your sentences?
_______ 22. Did you check for usage mistakes? *(subject/verb agreement, a/an choices, contractions, verb tenses, pronoun/antecedent agreement, pronoun cases, degrees of adjectives, double negatives, etc.)*
_______ 23. Did you put your revised and edited paper in the Rough Draft folder?

FINAL PAPER CHECK

_______ 24. Did you write the final paper in pencil?
_______ 25. Did you center the title on the top line and center your name under the title?
_______ 26. Did you skip a line before starting the writing assignment?
_______ 27. Did you single-space, use wide margins, and write the final paper neatly?
_______ 28. Did you staple your papers in this order: final paper on top, rough draft in the middle, and prewriting map on the bottom? Did you put them in the Final Paper folder?

Notes:

Classroom Practice 25

Name:______________________________ Date:______________

GRAMMAR

▶ **Exercise 1:** Classify each sentence.

1. __________ Oh, no! Yesterday, my oldest brother ran into Mr. Cobb's mailbox with Mom's new car!

2. __________ Jennifer and I worked yesterday on our science project for Mr. Smith's biology class.

SKILLS

▶ **Exercise 2:** Use a slash to separate each run-on sentence below. Then, correct the run-on sentences by rewriting them as indicated by the labels in parentheses at the end of each sentence.

1. Mother turned the key the car started. (**CX, when**) (1)

   ____

2. Mother turned the key the car started. (**CX, until**) (2)

   ____

3. Mother turned the key the car would not start. (**CX, even though**) (1)

   ____

4. The sun rose again the farmers were busy with chores. (**CX, before**) (1)

   ____

5. The little boy smiled the clown gave him a balloon. (**CX, after**) (2)

   ____

▶ **Exercise 3:** Identify each type of sentence by writing the correct label in the blank. (**Labels: S, F, SCS, SCV, CD, CX**)

__________ 1. As soon as I arrived, I began looking for my friends.
__________ 2. Our dog jumped and scratched at the door.
__________ 3. Racing from door to door with the good news.
__________ 4. The Christmas presents were piled around the tree.
__________ 5. I called, yet my friend did not answer the phone.
__________ 6. During the movie, Chris and Doug ate popcorn.
__________ 7. Since I do not have a bicycle, I usually walk to school.
__________ 8. When I get finished, I can go home.
__________ 9. The cold, blustery wind whipped around us and froze our cheeks.

EDITING

▶ **Exercise 4:** Correct each mistake. **Editing Guide: End Marks: 3 Capitals: 9 Commas: 2 Apostrophes: 2 Homonyms: 2 Subject-Verb Agreement: 4 Periods: 2 Misspelled Words: 1**

as they complete there tour of washington d c warrens family pause on the steps of the lincoln memorial for won last picture his mom gets everyones attention and snap the picture on the count of three mom warn everyone not to move becuz she want another shot

Notes:

Classroom Practice 26

Name:____ Date:__________________

GRAMMAR

▶ **Exercise 1:** Classify each sentence.

1. __________ Yikes! My paper and pencil flew across the aisle and landed at Ms. Simpson's feet!

2. __________ She and he talked excitedly to their friends during the morning break.

SKILLS

▶ **Exercise 2:** Identify each type of sentence by writing the correct label in the blank. (**Labels: S, F, SCS, SCV, CD, CX**)

__________ 1. I love to dance; I take lessons in jazz and tap.
__________ 2. In the spring, Crystal and Kate will play softball.
__________ 3. Gathered her books and supplies.
__________ 4. When the bell rang, the students left.
__________ 5. The snow melted when the sun came out.
__________ 6. You cannot go with us to the museum; unfortunately, you forgot your permission slip.
__________ 7. At lunch, teachers and students chatter noisily in the cafeteria.
__________ 8. The shiniest red sports car in the parking lot.
__________ 9. Before the comedian finished his joke, the crowd erupted with laughter.
__________ 10. The young mother and her two children waited patiently at the checkout.

▶ **Exercise 3:** Use a slash to separate each run-on sentence below. Then, correct the run-on sentences by rewriting them as indicated by the labels in parentheses at the end of each sentence.

1. The water was calm we walked along the beach. (**CX, as**) (**2**)
____
2. Tom was tired he enjoyed the game. (**CX, although**) (**1**)
____
3. Anna can draw well she entered an art contest. (**CX, since**) (**1**)
____
4. I always eat popcorn I am upset. (**CX, when**) (**2**)
____
5. I will go to the concert you will go with me. (**CX, if**) (**2**)
____

EDITING

▶ **Exercise 4:** Correct each mistake. **Editing Guide: End Marks: 5 Capitals: 11 Commas: 2 Apostrophes: 1 Homonyms: 2 A/An: 2 Subject-Verb Agreement: 2 Misspelled Words: 2**

raymond julias brother graduated from ohio state university with an dagree in nurseing in may he have had fifteen job offers in too weeks most employers offers him an bonus four signing with them he is getting more job offers every day i wish i had his problem

Notes:

Classroom Practice 27

Name:______________________________ Date:______________

GRAMMAR

Exercise 1: Classify each sentence.

1. __________ The new advisor quietly waited outside the President's office.

2. __________ Wow! Look at the enormous tires on Jeremy's new truck!

SKILLS

Exercise 2: Use a slash to separate each run-on sentence below. Then, correct the run-on sentences by rewriting them as indicated by the labels in parentheses at the end of each sentence.

1. We did not go to bed the movie was over. (**CX, until**) (**2**)
____

2. I watch scary movies I have trouble going to sleep. (**CX, whenever**) (**1**)
____

3. Jennifer was not allowed to have dessert she ate her vegetables. (**CX, until**) (**2**)
____

4. The girl was laughing no one seemed to notice. (**CX, although**) (**1**)
____

5. You must clean your room I will pay your allowance. (**CX, before**) (**2**)
____

Exercise 3: Identify each type of sentence by writing the correct label in the blank. (**Labels: S, F, SCS, SCV, CD, CX**)

__________ 1. You left your bicycle out in the rain; consequently, it rusted.
__________ 2. I love to read, and I go to the library at least twice a week.
__________ 3. During the musical, Jan and Joe sang a duet.
__________ 4. During the summer, when the games were over.
__________ 5. When I heard the noise, I ran to the window.
__________ 6. The ice melted after the sun came out.
__________ 7. My sisters waved good-bye and left for the concert.
__________ 8. Since I do not drive a car, I usually walk or ride a bus.
__________ 9. Eat balanced meals every day, and you will be healthier.
__________ 10. The salesman walked to the door and rang the doorbell.

EDITING

Exercise 4: Correct each mistake. **Editing Guide: End Marks: 2 Capitals: 13 Commas: 3 Apostrophes: 1 Homonyms: 1 Subject-Verb Agreement: 2 Periods: 1 Misspelled Words: 2**

did you no that sir arthur conan doyles famous detective character sherlock holmes were inspired by his medacal school professor dr joseph bell dad have all the sherlock holmes storys

Notes:

Chapter 6 Checkup 28

Name:____ Date:________________

GRAMMAR

Exercise 1: Classify each sentence.

1. __________ Dan's three fishing buddies idly sat in their boat for a relaxing day at the lake.

2. __________ Mercy! All the newborn babies in the nursery cried loudly throughout the night!

3. __________ Did the alumni of our college meet and talk together after the football game?

SKILLS

Exercise 2: Identify each type of sentence by writing the correct label in the blank. (**Labels: S, F, SCS, SCV, CD, CX**)

__________ 1. The wind whistled and howled during the night.
__________ 2. The glass door at the theatre's entrance.
__________ 3. A summer thunderstorm can be quite scary.
__________ 4. When Kyle finished his project, he treated himself to a movie.
__________ 5. Sports are fun, but they can be dangerous.
__________ 6. He didn't stop until he crossed the finish line.
__________ 7. Adam and Allison are planning a June wedding in England.
__________ 8. We like our new camera; however, it was expensive.

Exercise 3: Use a slash to separate each run-on sentence below. Then, correct the run-on sentences by rewriting them as indicated by the labels in parentheses at the end of each sentence.

1. The road was bumpy I drove slowly. (**CX, because**) (1)

____

2. The lights went out Kristi turned on the flashlight. (**CX, after**) (1)

____

3. I like to read I go to bed. (**CX, before**) (2)

____

4. Dale jumped he heard a loud noise. (**CX, when**) (2)

____

EDITING

Exercise 4: Correct each mistake. **Editing Guide: End Marks: 3 Capitals: 9 Commas: 1 Apostrophes: 2 Homonyms: 2 A/An: 1 Subject-Verb Agreement: 1 Periods: 2 Misspelled Words: 1**

ella didnt finish her homework for mr browns algebra class because back-to-back episodes of her favorite show were on last night after she recieved an note too her parents from mr brown she decided her priorities was not in order she knew their would be no tv tonight

Notes:

Classroom Practice 29

Name:____________________ Date:__________

INDEPENDENT PRACTICE & REVISED SENTENCES

1. **Write a Practice Sentence according to the labels you choose.**
   Use SN/SP V as your main labels. You may use the other labels in any order and as many times as you wish in order to make a Practice Sentence.
   Chapter 6 labels for a Practice Sentence: SN/SP, V, Adj, Adv, A, P, OP, PPA, C, HV, I, PNA
2. **Write a Revised Sentence. Use the following revision strategies: *synonym (syn), antonym (ant), word change (wc), added word (add), deleted word (delete),* or *no change (nc)*. Under each word, write the abbreviation of the revision strategy you use.**

Labels: ____________________

Practice: ____________________

Revised: ____________________

Strategies: ____________________

Labels: ____________________

Practice: ____________________

Revised: ____________________

Strategies: ____________________

Labels: ____________________

Practice: ____________________

Revised: ____________________

Strategies: ____________________

Notes:

Chapter 6 Writing Evaluation Guide

Name:_______________________________ Date:_______________

ROUGH DRAFT CHECK

_______ 1. Did you write your rough draft in pencil?
_______ 2. Did you write the correct headings on the first seven lines of your paper?
_______ 3. Did you use extra wide margins and skip every other line?
_______ 4. Did you write a title at the end of your rough draft?
_______ 5. Did you place your edited rough draft in your Rough Draft folder?

REVISING CHECK

_______ 6. Did you identify the purpose, type of writing, and audience?
_______ 7. Did you check for a topic, topic sentence, and sentences supporting the topic?
_______ 8. Did you check sentences for the right order, and did you combine, rearrange, or delete sentences when necessary?
_______ 9. Did you check for a variety of simple, compound, and complex sentences?
_______ 10. Did you check for any left out, repeated, or unnecessary words?
_______ 11. Did you check for the best choice of words by replacing or deleting unclear words?
_______ 12. Did you check the content for interest and creativity?
_______ 13. Did you check the voice to make sure the writing says what you want it to say?

EDITING CHECK

_______ 14. Did you indent each paragraph?
_______ 15. Did you put an end mark at the end of every sentence?
_______ 16. Did you capitalize the first word of every sentence?
_______ 17. Did you check for all other capitalization mistakes?
_______ 18. Did you check for all punctuation mistakes? *(commas, periods, apostrophes, quotation marks, underlining)*
_______ 19. Did you check for misspelled words and for incorrect homonym choices?
_______ 20. Did you check for incorrect spellings of plural and possessive forms?
_______ 21. Did you check for correct construction and punctuation of your sentences?
_______ 22. Did you check for usage mistakes? *(subject/verb agreement, a/an choices, contractions, verb tenses, pronoun/antecedent agreement, pronoun cases, degrees of adjectives, double negatives, etc.)*
_______ 23. Did you put your revised and edited paper in the Rough Draft folder?

FINAL PAPER CHECK

_______ 24. Did you write the final paper in pencil?
_______ 25. Did you center the title on the top line and center your name under the title?
_______ 26. Did you skip a line before starting the writing assignment?
_______ 27. Did you single-space, use wide margins, and write the final paper neatly?
_______ 28. Did you staple your papers in this order: final paper on top, rough draft in the middle, and prewriting map on the bottom? Did you put them in the Final Paper folder?

Notes:

Classroom Practice 30

Name:________________________________ Date:______________

GRAMMAR

▶ **Exercise 1:** Classify each sentence.

1. __________ Wow! He gave an outstanding speech!

2. __________ After school, Terrance and I played a quick game of basketball before dinner.

▶ **Exercise 2:** Use Sentence 2 and complete the table below.

List the Noun Used	List the Noun Job	Singular or Plural	Common or Proper	Simple Subject	Simple Predicate

SKILLS

▶ **Exercise 3:** (1) Underline the verb or verb phrase. (2) Identify the verb tense by writing **1** for present tense, **2** for past tense, or **3** for future tense. (3) Write the past-tense form. (4) Write **R** for Regular or **I** for Irregular.

	Verb Tense	Main Verb Past Tense Form	R or I
1. My sister swims every weekend.			
2. We laughed at his funny jokes.			
3. The small boy ran after the bus.			
4. My parents go to town on Monday nights.			
5. The pitcher throws the ball fast.			
6. I washed the dog last Saturday.			
7. I will leave soon for the grocery store.			
8. We walk a mile every day.			
9. The fireworks will begin at eight o'clock.			
10. Colorful leaves rustle in the chilly autumn wind.			

EDITING

▶ **Exercise 4:** Correct each mistake. **Editing Guide: End Marks: 3 Capitals: 9 Commas: 3 Apostrophes: 3 Homonyms: 3 A/An: 1 Subject-Verb Agreement: 3 Underlining: 1 Misspelled Words: 1**

matthew climb into his mothers lap for story time he listen attentively as his mothers soft voise flows threw the words of hans christian andersens fairy tail the ugly duckling soon his eyes become heavy with sleep and he drift away into an world full of fairy tails

Notes:

Classroom Practice 31

Name:______________________________ Date:______________

GRAMMAR

▶ **Exercise 1:** Classify each sentence.

1. __________ Give an explanation and an apology to Mom and Dad for your absence during dinner.

2. __________ He and she have not sent their vacation photographs to their friends in Utah and Ohio.

▶ **Exercise 2:** Use Sentence 2 above and complete the table below.

List the Noun Used	List the Noun Job	Singular or Plural	Common or Proper	Simple Subject	Simple Predicate

SKILLS

▶ **Exercise 3:** (1) Underline the verb or verb phrase. (2) Identify the verb tense by writing **1** for present tense, **2** for past tense, or **3** for future tense. (3) Write the past-tense form. (4) Write **R** for Regular or **I** for Irregular.

	Verb Tense	Main Verb Past Tense Form	R or I
1. The judges will choose the winner tonight.			
2. Our pool needed chemicals.			
3. Aunt Sue makes delicious peanut brittle.			
4. Sandy had given many haircuts to ladies.			
5. The rude boy has argued with everyone.			

▶ **Exercise 4:** List the present-tense and past-tense helping verbs.

Present Tense	1.	2.	3.	4.	5.	6.	7.
Past Tense	1.	2.	3.	4.	5.		

EDITING

▶ **Exercise 5:** Correct each mistake. **Editing Guide: End Marks: 4 Capitals: 8 Commas: 5 Apostrophes: 1 Homonyms: 3 Subject-Verb Agreement: 3 Misspelled Words: 1**

mother always fixes uncle leos favorite dessert for christmas dinner he are her only brother she and her five sisters prepares turkey ham dressing saleds homemade rolls and desserts four our annual christmas gathering even hour neighbors comes to hour feast

Notes:

Classroom Practice 32

Name:______________________________ Date:______________

GRAMMAR

▶ **Exercise 1:** Classify each sentence.

1. __________ Suddenly, the heavyweight boxer in the ring threw a knockout punch at his opponent!

2. __________ Darcy and I checked the prices and availability of the new computer games today.

SKILLS

▶ **Exercise 2:** (1) Underline the verb or verb phrase. (2) Identify the verb tense by writing **1** for present tense, **2** for past tense, or **3** for future tense. (3) Write the past-tense form. (4) Write **R** for Regular or **I** for Irregular.

	Verb Tense	Main Verb Past Tense Form	R or I
1. We are picking tomatoes in your garden.			
2. The puppy napped in a corner of the room.			
3. Will Bobby catch the ball on first base?			
4. The butcher will slice you a thick steak.			
5. The baby goat has been sleeping in the hay.			
6. Our truck will be sold at the auction.			
7. The artist paints one picture every week.			
8. Were you watching those children in the pool?			
9. Have you studied your science lesson?			
10. The author was writing about a boy and his dog.			

▶ **Exercise 3:** List the present-tense and past-tense helping verbs below.

Present Tense	1.	2.	3.	4.	5.	6.	7.
Past Tense	1.	2.	3.	4.	5.		

EDITING

▶ **Exercise 4:** Correct each mistake. **Editing Guide: End Marks: 5 Capitals: 13 Commas: 1 Apostrophes: 1 Homonyms: 5 A/An: 2 Subject-Verb Agreement: 6 Periods: 2 Misspelled Words: 1**

tony stare longingly through the window at jaspers pet store he wants sew much too take an puppy home but he nose that his family are not allowed to have pets in the apartament he is about two leave when mr jasper knock on the window and motion for tony too come in tony is thrilled when mr jasper offer him an job tony promise to be the best employee ever

Notes:

Chapter 7 Checkup 33

Name:________________________________ Date:________________

GRAMMAR

Exercise 1: Classify each sentence.

1. __________ Send an e-mail to Aunt Natalie and Uncle Drew about our family's Christmas party.

2. __________ Mercy! That large herd of cattle trampled and destroyed those young saplings!

3. __________ Are the old machines in the clothing factory finally showing signs of extreme wear?

SKILLS

Exercise 2: (1) Underline the verb or verb phrase. (2) Identify the verb tense by writing **1** for present tense, **2** for past tense, or **3** for future tense. (3) Write the past-tense form. (4) Write **R** for Regular or **I** for Irregular.

	Verb Tense	Main Verb Past Tense Form	R or I
1. Our family leaves for California on Saturday.			
2. Traffic moved carefully through the construction zone.			
3. The carpenter carries his tools with him.			
4. The birds are flying over the lake.			
5. The pitcher throws the ball hard and fast.			
6. Our dogs have eaten all their food.			
7. I see three kittens in the basket.			
8. Mom has cooked my favorite meal.			
9. The wind will blow hard from the north.			
10. My sisters had practiced ballet today.			

Exercise 3: List the present-tense and past-tense helping verbs below.

Present Tense	1.	2.	3.	4.	5.	6.	7.
Past Tense	1.	2.	3.	4.	5.		

EDITING

Exercise 4: Correct each mistake. **Editing Guide: End Marks: 4 Capitals: 18 Commas: 3 Quotation Marks: 2 Apostrophes: 1 Subject-Verb Agreement: 3 Misspelled Words: 1**

harriets favorite christmas carol is silver bells by jay livingston and ray evans harriet play this song and other holiday favorates at the carter rest home on christmas eve the residents and staff sings as harriet plays before harriet leaves she give gifts candy and cards to everyone

Notes:

Classroom Practice 34

Name:______________________________ Date:______________

INDEPENDENT PRACTICE & REVISED SENTENCES

1. **Write a Practice Sentence according to the labels you choose.**
   Use SN/SP V-t DO as your main labels. You may use the other labels in any order and as many times as you wish in order to make a Practice Sentence.
   Chapter 7 labels for a Practice Sentence: SN/SP, V-t, DO, Adj, Adv, A, P, OP, PPA, C, HV, I, PNA
2. **Write a Revised Sentence. Use the following revision strategies: *synonym (syn), antonym (ant), word change (wc), added word (add), deleted word (delete),* or *no change (nc)*. Under each word, write the abbreviation of the revision strategy you use.**

Labels: ______________________________

Practice: ______________________________

Revised: ______________________________

Strategies: ______________________________

Labels: ______________________________

Practice: ______________________________

Revised: ______________________________

Strategies: ______________________________

Labels: ______________________________

Practice: ______________________________

Revised: ______________________________

Strategies: ______________________________

Notes:

Chapter 7 Writing Evaluation Guide

Name:________________________________ Date:________________

ROUGH DRAFT CHECK

______ 1. Did you write your rough draft in pencil?
______ 2. Did you write the correct headings on the first seven lines of your paper?
______ 3. Did you use extra wide margins and skip every other line?
______ 4. Did you write a title at the end of your rough draft?
______ 5. Did you place your edited rough draft in your Rough Draft folder?

REVISING CHECK

______ 6. Did you identify the purpose, type of writing, and audience?
______ 7. Did you check for a topic, topic sentence, and sentences supporting the topic?
______ 8. Did you check sentences for the right order, and did you combine, rearrange, or delete sentences when necessary?
______ 9. Did you check for a variety of simple, compound, and complex sentences?
______ 10. Did you check for any left out, repeated, or unnecessary words?
______ 11. Did you check for the best choice of words by replacing or deleting unclear words?
______ 12. Did you check the content for interest and creativity?
______ 13. Did you check the voice to make sure the writing says what you want it to say?

EDITING CHECK

______ 14. Did you indent each paragraph?
______ 15. Did you put an end mark at the end of every sentence?
______ 16. Did you capitalize the first word of every sentence?
______ 17. Did you check for all other capitalization mistakes?
______ 18. Did you check for all punctuation mistakes? *(commas, periods, apostrophes, quotation marks, underlining)*
______ 19. Did you check for misspelled words and for incorrect homonym choices?
______ 20. Did you check for incorrect spellings of plural and possessive forms?
______ 21. Did you check for correct construction and punctuation of your sentences?
______ 22. Did you check for usage mistakes? *(subject/verb agreement, a/an choices, contractions, verb tenses, pronoun/antecedent agreement, pronoun cases, degrees of adjectives, double negatives, etc.)*
______ 23. Did you put your revised and edited paper in the Rough Draft folder?

FINAL PAPER CHECK

______ 24. Did you write the final paper in pencil?
______ 25. Did you center the title on the top line and center your name under the title?
______ 26. Did you skip a line before starting the writing assignment?
______ 27. Did you single-space, use wide margins, and write the final paper neatly?
______ 28. Did you staple your papers in this order: final paper on top, rough draft in the middle, and prewriting map on the bottom? Did you put them in the Final Paper folder?

Notes:

Classroom Practice 35

Name:______________________________ Date:______________

GRAMMAR

▶ **Exercise 1:** Classify each sentence.

1. __________ Did Grandfather send his collection of rare stamps to several museums for display?

2. __________ My mom and dad were cheering loudly for us during our soccer game today!

SKILLS

▶ **Exercise 2:** Change the underlined present-tense verbs in Paragraph 1 to past-tense verbs in Paragraph 2.

Paragraph 1: Present Tense

My brother **is** a student of the martial arts. He **loves** it and **practices** all the time. He **shouts** and **kicks** his bare foot high in the air. I **shout** at him to stop, but he **goes** right on. I **glare** at him and his black belt. This constant practice **has** to stop! I **kick** my chair out of the way and **jump** in front of him. I **wave** my arms, **grunt** loudly, and **shuffle** my feet. I **hold** my funny-looking stance in front of him. I **dare** him to practice one more time in front of me. He **grins** at me and **bows**. Then, he **walks** out and **leaves** me in peace.

Paragraph 2: Past Tense

My brother ______ a student of the martial arts. He __________ it and ______________ all the time. He ______________ and __________ his bare foot high in the air. I ______________ at him to stop, but he ____________ right on. I _________________ at him and his black belt. This constant practice _________ to stop! I ___________ my chair out of the way and ______________ in front of him. I ______________ my arms, _______________ loudly, and ________________ my feet. I __________ my funny-looking stance in front of him. I _______________ him to practice one more time in front of me. He _________________ at me and ______________ . Then, he ______________ out and ___________ me in peace.

EDITING

▶ **Exercise 3:** Correct each mistake. **Editing Guide: End Marks: 7 Capitals: 10 Commas: 5 Apostrophes: 1 Homonyms: 4 A/An: 1 Subject-Verb Agreement: 7 Periods: 2 Misspelled Words: 1**

elaine gracefully walk across the stage in her shimmering gown she nervously grip the microphone but her smile never fade the music begins to play over the speakers elaine weights fore her cue and she begin to sing her voice flows beautifully threw the song and she smile as she completes the final verse she nose that she have finished an magical performence mr and mrs harris elaines parents claps and cheer louder than anyone in the big auditorium

Notes:

Classroom Practice 36

Name:______________________________ Date:______________

GRAMMAR

▶ **Exercise 1:** Classify each sentence.

1. __________ Are you introducing them at the wedding rehearsal tonight?

2. __________ Shhh! The baby is finally sleeping after a long afternoon of fretting and crying!

SKILLS

▶ **Exercise 2:** Change the underlined mixed-tense verbs in Paragraph 1 to **present-tense verbs** in Paragraph 2.

Paragraph 1: Mixed Tenses

Today **is** the first time I **had flown**, and I **was** very anxious. The airport **is** busy, and people **rushed** to get to their planes on time. On board, I **found** my assigned seat and **buckle** up as the flight attendant **demonstrates** the use of the oxygen masks. We **taxied** on the runway, **pause**, and then **raced** toward the sky. I **lost** my stomach as the wheels **bump** farewell to the earth. My clammy hands **unclench** slowly, and I gradually **relaxed**. I **grin** broadly as the refreshment cart **rattled** up the aisle. The snack **kept** my mind busy, and I **did** not **think** about flying.

Paragraph 2: Present Tense

Today _____ the first time I ____________ ____________, and I _________ very anxious. The airport _______ busy, and people ________ to get to their planes on time. On board, I ________ my assigned seat and ____________ up as the flight attendant ___________________ the use of the oxygen masks. We ___________ on the runway, ___________, and then ___________ toward the sky. I ___________ my stomach as the wheels ___________ farewell to the earth. My clammy hands _______________ slowly, and I gradually ___________. I _________ broadly as the refreshment cart _____________ up the aisle. The snack ___________ my mind busy, and I ___________ not ____________ about flying.

EDITING

▶ **Exercise 3:** Correct each mistake. **Editing Guide: End Marks: 6 Capitals: 9 Commas: 4 Apostrophes: 2 Homonyms: 7 A/An: 3 Subject-Verb Agreement: 6 Misspelled Words: 1**

the omelet sizzle on the stove as kristi pour a glass of orange juice elizabeth her sister arrange the plate and silverware on the trey and she neatly folds a cloth napkin kristi place an vase containing an single read rose in the corner of the tray the girls beams as they hand the trey too they're dad he smile and balances the tray with both hands dad winks at his daughers and he leads the weigh into there mothers bedroom for an mothers day surprise

Notes:

Classroom Practice 37

Name:______________________________ Date:______________

GRAMMAR

▶ **Exercise 1:** Classify each sentence.

1. __________ After dinner, Dad and my baby brother laughed and played in the hammock.

2. __________ The very swift planes certainly exceeded the speed of sound during their flights.

SKILLS

▶ **Exercise 2:** Write the four principal parts of the following verbs: **choose** and **jump**.

PRESENT	PAST	PAST PARTICIPLE	PRESENT PARTICIPLE
1. __________	3. __________	5. (**has**) __________	7. (**is**) __________
2. __________	4. __________	6. (**has**) __________	8. (**is**) __________

▶ **Exercise 3:** Change the underlined mixed-tense verbs in Paragraph 1 to present-tense verbs in Paragraph 2.

Paragraph 1: Mixed Tenses

My dad **was** a big lovable bear this morning. He **comes** into the kitchen and **gave** our mom a big bear hug while she **made** breakfast. Then, he **roams** through the house and **growled** at us kids to get up. While we **ate** breakfast, he **tells** us the latest jokes and **laughed** louder than anyone else. Then, he **gave** us a list of chores to do and **cautions** us to finish them. After he **leaves** the house, we **heard** our beloved bear around the trash cans. We **looked** at each other and **race** to the window. We **sighed** with relief. Our bear **is** only **taking** out the garbage!

Paragraph 2: Present Tense

My dad ______ a big lovable bear this morning. He ____________ into the kitchen and ___________ our mom a big bear hug while she ____________ breakfast. Then, he _____________ through the house and ______________ at us kids to get up. While we _________ breakfast, he _________ us the latest jokes and ___________ louder than anyone else. Then, he ___________ us a list of chores to do and ________________ us to finish them. After he ________________ the house, we __________ our beloved bear around the trash cans. We ___________ at each other and ___________ to the window. We ___________ with relief. Our bear ______ only ______________ out the garbage!

EDITING

▶ **Exercise 4:** Correct each mistake. **Editing Guide: End Marks: 5 Capitals: 12 Commas: 2 Apostrophes: 1 Homonyms: 2 A/An: 2 Subject-Verb Agreement: 6 Misspelled Words: 3**

aunt sally gather fresh honey from her behives every morning i loves too watch from aunt sallys kitchen window as the bees buzz angerly around her like an dark cloud they swarms around and threatens her with there nasty stings thankfully she always wear protective clotheing and an netted hood i help aunt sally bottle her honey and uncle lester sell the honey in town

Notes:

Classroom Practice 38

Name:________________________________ Date:______________

GRAMMAR

▶ **Exercise 1:** Classify each sentence.

1. __________ Call me for an appointment at your earliest convenience.

2. __________ Would you study with me after school for the English and math exams?

SKILLS

▶ **Exercise 2:** Write the four principal parts of the following verbs: **throw** and **whisper**.

PRESENT	PAST	PAST PARTICIPLE	PRESENT PARTICIPLE
1. __________	3. __________	5. (has) __________	7. (is) __________
2. __________	4. __________	6. (has) __________	8. (is) __________

▶ **Exercise 3:** Change the underlined mixed-tense verbs in Paragraph 1 to past-tense verbs in Paragraph 2.

Paragraph 1: Mixed Tenses

Blinky **was** my beloved computer. He **helps** me when I **check** my homework. I **am** tired tonight, so I **program** Blinky to work my math problems. When my mom **looks** over them, she **told** me all my problems **are** wrong! My mouth **dropped** open. I **march** back into my room and **glare** at Blinky. I **tapped** my fingers angrily beside Blinky's keyboard. I finally **decide** to check Blinky's command system. Then, I **groan** loudly. It **isn't** Blinky's fault after all. It **is** Dad's fault. He **had programmed** Blinky not to do my homework.

Paragraph 2: Past Tense

Blinky _______ my beloved computer. He ___________ me when I _____________ my homework. I ______ tired tonight, so I ____________________ Blinky to work my math problems. When my mom ________________ over them, she ___________ me all my problems __________ wrong! My mouth _____________ open. I ________________ back into my room and _____________ at Blinky. I ____________ my fingers angrily beside Blinky's keyboard. I finally ______________ to check Blinky's command system. Then, I ________________ loudly. It ___________ Blinky's fault after all. It _______ Dad's fault. He ________ ____________________ Blinky not to do my homework.

EDITING

▶ **Exercise 4:** Correct each mistake in the present-tense paragraph. **Editing Guide: End Marks: 6 Capitals: 6 Commas: 7 Apostrophes: 1 Homonyms: 3 Verb Tense: 6 Misspelled Words: 2**

agnes my calico cat loved to look out the window doug my brother loved to pull her tale as she sits on the window sill and stared outside agnes should be my brothers cat becaus she pouts when he was not around she looks fore him every day after school and she was never disapointed doug comes in sneaked up behind her and pulls her tail what a pear of comedians

Notes:

Chapter 8 Checkup 39

Name:______________________________ Date:______________

GRAMMAR

▶ **Exercise 1:** Classify each sentence.

1. __________ Ouch! I bumped my elbow on the edge of that table in the back of the room!

2. __________ Yesterday, a family of wild bears slowly lumbered to their cave for the winter.

3. __________ Did my picky little brother eat one raisin from the middle of his oatmeal cookie?

SKILLS

▶ **Exercise 2:** Write the four principal parts of the following verbs: **take** and **laugh**.

PRESENT	PAST	PAST PARTICIPLE	PRESENT PARTICIPLE
1. __________	3. __________	5. **(has)** __________	7. **(is)** __________
2. __________	4. __________	6. **(has)** __________	8. **(is)** __________

▶ **Exercise 3:** Change the underlined mixed-tense verbs in Paragraph 1 to past-tense verbs in Paragraph 2.

Paragraph 1: Mixed Tenses

Chores always **send** me into orbit! They **spoil** a perfect day. My mom **told** me that chores **develop** responsibility. My dad **tells** me that they **build** character, and my little brother **tells** me that he **is** too young for chores. Of course, I **argue** with my mom, **sigh** at my dad, and **glare** at my little brother. However, my mom **has** the perfect solution. She **waved** my allowance in front of my nose. It **is** funny how my chores suddenly **became** more bearable. I **agree** with my mom, **nod** at my dad, but still **glared** at my little brother.

Paragraph 2: Past Tense

Chores always ________ me into orbit! They __________ a perfect day. My mom ________ me that chores __________ responsibility. My dad ________ me that they __________ character, and my little brother ________ me that he ________ too young for chores. Of course, I __________ with my mom, __________ at my dad, and __________ at my little brother. However, my mom ________ the perfect solution. She ________ my allowance in front of my nose. It ________ funny how my chores suddenly __________ more bearable. I ________ with my mom, __________ at my dad, but still __________ at my little brother.

EDITING

▶ **Exercise 4:** Correct each mistake. **Editing Guide: End Marks: 3 Capitals: 6 Commas: 2 Apostrophes: 1 Subject-Verb Agreement: 1 Periods: 1 Misspelled Words: 1**

ms turleys science class made a miniature rocket and they launched it yesterday a parent filmed it and the students watched it on tv during class today the launch were truly spectackular

Notes:

Chapter 8 Writing Evaluation Guide

Name:______________________________ Date:______________

ROUGH DRAFT CHECK

_____ 1. Did you write your rough draft in pencil?
_____ 2. Did you write the correct headings on the first seven lines of your paper?
_____ 3. Did you use extra wide margins and skip every other line?
_____ 4. Did you write a title at the end of your rough draft?
_____ 5. Did you place your edited rough draft in your Rough Draft folder?

REVISING CHECK

_____ 6. Did you identify the purpose, type of writing, and audience?
_____ 7. Did you check for a topic, topic sentence, and sentences supporting the topic?
_____ 8. Did you check sentences for the right order, and did you combine, rearrange, or delete sentences when necessary?
_____ 9. Did you check for a variety of simple, compound, and complex sentences?
_____ 10. Did you check for any left out, repeated, or unnecessary words?
_____ 11. Did you check for the best choice of words by replacing or deleting unclear words?
_____ 12. Did you check the content for interest and creativity?
_____ 13. Did you check the voice to make sure the writing says what you want it to say?

EDITING CHECK

_____ 14. Did you indent each paragraph?
_____ 15. Did you put an end mark at the end of every sentence?
_____ 16. Did you capitalize the first word of every sentence?
_____ 17. Did you check for all other capitalization mistakes?
_____ 18. Did you check for all punctuation mistakes? *(commas, periods, apostrophes, quotation marks, underlining)*
_____ 19. Did you check for misspelled words and for incorrect homonym choices?
_____ 20. Did you check for incorrect spellings of plural and possessive forms?
_____ 21. Did you check for correct construction and punctuation of your sentences?
_____ 22. Did you check for usage mistakes? *(subject/verb agreement, a/an choices, contractions, verb tenses, pronoun/antecedent agreement, pronoun cases, degrees of adjectives, double negatives, etc.)*
_____ 23. Did you put your revised and edited paper in the Rough Draft folder?

FINAL PAPER CHECK

_____ 24. Did you write the final paper in pencil?
_____ 25. Did you center the title on the top line and center your name under the title?
_____ 26. Did you skip a line before starting the writing assignment?
_____ 27. Did you single-space, use wide margins, and write the final paper neatly?
_____ 28. Did you staple your papers in this order: final paper on top, rough draft in the middle, and prewriting map on the bottom? Did you put them in the Final Paper folder?

Notes:

Classroom Practice 40

Name:____ Date:________________

GRAMMAR

▸ **Exercise 1:** Classify each sentence.

1. __________ Golly! That loud dynamite blast gave me a huge scare during lunchtime!
2. __________ Today, the patrolman gave Jared a warning ticket for speeding in a school zone.

SKILLS & EDITING

▸ **Exercise 2:** Punctuate the sentences below. **Editing Guide: End Marks: 8 Capitals: 21 Commas: 6 Quotation Marks: 12 Underlined Explanatory Words: 4 Apostrophes: 4 Periods: 4**

1. jeremy could you order pizza for ms smiths class courtney asked
2. courtney asked jeremy could you order pizza for ms smiths class
3. jeremy courtney asked could you order pizza for ms smiths class
4. jeremy could you order pizza for ms smiths class courtney asked her students won the math contest at riverdale middle school they are going to celebrate with a pizza party

SKILLS & EDITING

▸ **Exercise 3:** Punctuate the sentences below. **Editing Guide: End Marks: 7 Capitals: 37 Commas: 4 Quotation Marks: 10 Underlined Explanatory Words: 4 Apostrophes: 1**

1. travis exclaimed darren and i are going to palm springs to the jefferson golf tournament
2. darren and i are going to palm springs to the jefferson golf tournament exclaimed travis
3. darren and i travis exclaimed are going to palm springs to the jefferson golf tournament
4. travis exclaimed darren and i are going to palm springs to the jefferson golf tournament do you think danny and leroy can go with us its three weeks from saturday

Notes:

Classroom Practice 41

Name:______________________________ Date:______________

GRAMMAR

Exercise 1: Classify each sentence.

1. __________ Give Kerry and Lana several questions for their interview with the new mayor.

2. __________ The terrific salesman in the electronics store gave us a fantastic deal on a computer.

SKILLS & EDITING

Exercise 2: Punctuate the story below. **Editing Guide: End Marks: 15 Capitals: 24 Commas: 9 Quotation Marks: 16 Underlined Explanatory Words: 8 Apostrophes: 2**

jean i went fishing yesterday henry said

jean asked did you catch anything

yes i caught a fish so big that i couldnt get him into the boat exclaimed henry

wow what happened then asked jean excitedly

that big fish pulled me overboard henry declared loudly

well did you have to swim jean wanted to know

henry laughed hysterically and said no i landed on his back and we went on a wild ride

jean glared at henry and muttered you got that stupid tale out of a book i knew you didnt make up a story that good by yourself which book did you read

Notes:

Classroom Practice 42

Name:______________________________ Date:______________

GRAMMAR

▶ **Exercise 1:** Classify each sentence.

1. __________ Quick! Give me my camera for an exceptional shot of the koalas in the trees!

2. __________ As a reward, Mom and Dad opened me an account at our bank yesterday.

SKILLS & EDITING

▶ **Exercise 2:** Punctuate the sentences below. **Editing Guide: End Marks: 5 Capitals: 14 Commas: 9 Quotation Marks: 12 Underlined Explanatory Words: 4 Apostrophes: 1**

1. mom said joe i want you to do the dishes tonight

2. joe i want you to do the dishes tonight mom said

3. joe mom said i want you to do the dishes tonight

4. joe i want you to do the dishes tonight said mom i have a meeting after dinner

   and i wont get back in time to do them

SKILLS & EDITING

▶ **Exercise 3:** Punctuate the sentences below. **Editing Guide: End Marks: 6 Capitals: 16 Commas: 8 Quotation Marks: 6 Underlined Explanatory Words: 2 Apostrophes: 2**

1. joe i want you to do the dishes tonight said mom because i have a meeting

   after dinner it will be late when i get back and i wont have time to do them

2. mom said joe i want you to do the dishes tonight because i have a meeting after dinner

   it will be late when i get back and i wont have time to do them your grandmother will be

   here soon and you can show her your new game you also have snacks in the refrigerator

Notes:

Chapter 9 Checkup 43

Name:________________________________ Date:________________

GRAMMAR

▶ **Exercise 1:** Classify each sentence.

1. __________ Pass me the salt and pepper for my baked potato and sliced tomatoes.

2. __________ Mercy! I have not written you a letter in a long time!

3. __________ The proud firemen showed the reporter their new fire equipment from the city.

SKILLS & EDITING

▶ **Exercise 2:** Part 1. Punctuate the story below. **Editing Guide: End Marks: 4 Capitals: 6 Commas: 6 Quotation Marks: 8 Homonyms: 5 Misspelled Words: 2**

dad it is just to hot outside too work in the garden dave grumbled as he grudgeingly picked up the garden tools and followed his father too the garden besides dave continued to much sun is definately bad for your health dave emphasized what he just said by squinting at the bright son and by wiping his brow with his sleeve actually you could get a sunstroke he said lamely as he worked beside his father

SKILLS & EDITING

▶ **Exercise 3:** Part 2. Punctuate the rest of the story below. **Editing Guide: End Marks: 5 Capitals: 11 Commas: 11 Quotation Marks: 14 Apostrophes: 4 Homonyms: 3**

his fathers eyes danced with laughter as he said i think thats called a heatstroke dave

sunstroke—heatstroke it doesnt matter dave said it all amounts too a garden stroke

well his father replied i thought you might enjoy going too the lake after we have finished but it looks like you might be to stroked out

you know dad dave blurted if we work faster well get less sun

Notes:

Classroom Practice 44

Name:______________________________ Date:______________

INDEPENDENT PRACTICE & REVISED SENTENCES

1. Write a Practice Sentence according to the labels you choose.
   Use **SN/SP V-t IO DO** as your main labels. You may use the other labels in any order and as many times as you wish in order to make a Practice Sentence.
   Chapter 9 labels for a Practice Sentence: SN/SP, V-t, IO, DO, Adj, Adv, A, P, OP, PPA, C, HV, I, PNA
2. Write a Revised Sentence. Use the following revision strategies: *synonym (syn), antonym (ant), word change (wc), added word (add), deleted word (delete),* or *no change (nc)*. Under each word, write the abbreviation of the revision strategy you use.

Labels: ______________________________

Practice: ______________________________

Revised: ______________________________

Strategies: ______________________________

Labels: ______________________________

Practice: ______________________________

Revised: ______________________________

Strategies: ______________________________

Labels: ______________________________

Practice: ______________________________

Revised: ______________________________

Strategies: ______________________________

Notes:

Chapter 9 Writing Evaluation Guide

Name:______________________________ Date:______________

ROUGH DRAFT CHECK

______ 1. Did you write your rough draft in pencil?
______ 2. Did you write the correct headings on the first seven lines of your paper?
______ 3. Did you use extra wide margins and skip every other line?
______ 4. Did you write a title at the end of your rough draft?
______ 5. Did you place your edited rough draft in your Rough Draft folder?

REVISING CHECK

______ 6. Did you identify the purpose, type of writing, and audience?
______ 7. Did you check for a topic, topic sentence, and sentences supporting the topic?
______ 8. Did you check sentences for the right order, and did you combine, rearrange, or delete sentences when necessary?
______ 9. Did you check for a variety of simple, compound, and complex sentences?
______ 10. Did you check for any left out, repeated, or unnecessary words?
______ 11. Did you check for the best choice of words by replacing or deleting unclear words?
______ 12. Did you check the content for interest and creativity?
______ 13. Did you check the voice to make sure the writing says what you want it to say?

EDITING CHECK

______ 14. Did you indent each paragraph?
______ 15. Did you put an end mark at the end of every sentence?
______ 16. Did you capitalize the first word of every sentence?
______ 17. Did you check for all other capitalization mistakes?
______ 18. Did you check for all punctuation mistakes? *(commas, periods, apostrophes, quotation marks, underlining)*
______ 19. Did you check for misspelled words and for incorrect homonym choices?
______ 20. Did you check for incorrect spellings of plural and possessive forms?
______ 21. Did you check for correct construction and punctuation of your sentences?
______ 22. Did you check for usage mistakes? *(subject/verb agreement, a/an choices, contractions, verb tenses, pronoun/antecedent agreement, pronoun cases, degrees of adjectives, double negatives, etc.)*
______ 23. Did you put your revised and edited paper in the Rough Draft folder?

FINAL PAPER CHECK

______ 24. Did you write the final paper in pencil?
______ 25. Did you center the title on the top line and center your name under the title?
______ 26. Did you skip a line before starting the writing assignment?
______ 27. Did you single-space, use wide margins, and write the final paper neatly?
______ 28. Did you staple your papers in this order: final paper on top, rough draft in the middle, and prewriting map on the bottom? Did you put them in the Final Paper folder?

Notes:

Classroom Practice 45

Name:______________________ Date:______________

GRAMMAR

Exercise 1: Classify each sentence.

1. __________ Did the boys and girls quietly listen to the librarian's story?

2. __________ During science class, the teacher showed Jeff a diagram of the human heart.

SKILLS

Exercise 2: For each noun, write the rule number and the plural form that follows the rule. Some nouns have two acceptable plural forms, but you should use the plural spellings that can be verified by these rules.

RULES FOR MAKING REGULAR NOUNS PLURAL

Add -s to nouns without special endings.
1. most singular nouns.

Add -es to nouns with these special endings:
2. ***ch, sh, z, s, ss, x.***
3. a consonant plus ***o***.
4. a consonant plus ***y***, change **y** to **i** before adding **es**.
5. ***f*** or ***fe***, change **f** or **fe** to **v** before adding **es**.

Add -s to nouns with these special endings:
6. ***f*** or ***ff***.
7. a vowel plus ***o***.
8. a vowel plus ***y***.

RULES FOR MAKING IRREGULAR NOUNS PLURAL
9. Change the spelling completely for the plural form.
10. Spell the same for both the singular and plural form.

	Rule	Plural Form		Rule	Plural Form
1. kite			11. woman		
2. try			12. video		
3. guess			13. half		
4. foot			14. chimney		
5. tooth			15. knife		
6. pulley			16. proof		
7. mystery			17. deer		
8. series			18. brush		
9. touch			19. radio		
10. cliff			20. veto		

EDITING

Exercise 3: Punctuate the Kay and Robert story, "Brotherless." (Part 1 of 5)
Editing Guide: End Marks: 6 Capitals: 7 Commas: 2 Quotation Marks: 6 Apostrophes: 1

kay looked at her brother and shook her head what did i do to deserve a brother like you she asked irritably

i have to admit robert replied with a wide smile that you are ONE lucky girl i guess you know that most girls would love to have a brother like me roberts blue eyes sparkled as he teased his twin sister

Notes:

Classroom Practice 46

Name:________________________________ Date:______________

GRAMMAR

▶ **Exercise 1:** Classify each sentence.

1. __________ Was the swimming instructor helping several new students with their backstroke?

2. __________ On the first day of school, Jill usually gives her teacher a delicious red apple.

SKILLS

▶ **Exercise 2:** For each noun, write the rule number and the plural form that follows the rule. Some nouns have two acceptable plural forms, but you should use the plural spellings that can be verified by these rules.

RULES FOR MAKING REGULAR NOUNS PLURAL

Add -s to nouns without special endings.

1. most singular nouns.

Add -es to nouns with these special endings:

2. ***ch, sh, z, s, ss, x.***
3. a consonant plus ***o***.
4. a consonant plus ***y***, change **y** to **i** before adding **es**.
5. ***f*** or ***fe***, change **f** or **fe** to **v** before adding **es**.

Add -s to nouns with these special endings:

6. ***f*** or ***ff***.
7. a vowel plus ***o***.
8. a vowel plus ***y***.

RULES FOR MAKING IRREGULAR NOUNS PLURAL

9. Change the spelling completely for the plural form.
10. Spell the same for both the singular and plural form.

	Rule	Plural Form		Rule	Plural Form
1. alley			11. brush		
2. leaf			12. video		
3. puff			13. potato		
4. sheep			14. icicle		
5. child			15. forty		
6. journey			16. bunch		
7. baby			17. goose		
8. mouse			18. salmon		
9. radio			19. pass		
10. self			20. sheriff		

EDITING

▶ **Exercise 3:** Punctuate the Kay and Robert story, "Brotherless." (Part 2 of 5)
Editing Guide: End Marks: 5 Capitals: 10 Commas: 7 Quotation Marks: 10 Apostrophes: 1

yeah right kay said sarcastically as she gathered her research materials from the library table most girls would love to have a brother like you if they enjoy being irritated all the time

now kay be fair robert said with mock hurt in his voice you know you couldnt live without me

kay replied dreamily as she walked toward the door you know i wonder what it would be like to be brotherless

Notes:

Classroom Practice 47

Name:______________________________ Date:______________

GRAMMAR

Exercise 1: Classify each sentence.

1. __________ Oh no! I chipped the rim of a goblet from my grandmother's collection of fine crystal!

2. __________ Yesterday, a pack of wild coyotes definitely gave us a scare in the canyon!

SKILLS

Exercise 2: For each noun, write the rule number and the plural form that follows the rule. Some nouns have two acceptable plural forms, but you should use the plural spellings that can be verified by these rules.

RULES FOR MAKING REGULAR NOUNS PLURAL

Add -s to nouns without special endings.

1. most singular nouns.

Add -es to nouns with these special endings:

2. ***ch, sh, z, s, ss, x.***
3. a consonant plus ***o.***
4. a consonant plus ***y,*** change **y** to **i** before adding **es.**
5. ***f*** or ***fe,*** change **f** or **fe** to **v** before adding **es.**

Add -s to nouns with these special endings:

6. ***f*** or ***ff.***
7. a vowel plus ***o.***
8. a vowel plus ***y.***

RULES FOR MAKING IRREGULAR NOUNS PLURAL

9. Change the spelling completely for the plural form.
10. Spell the same for both the singular and plural form.

	Rule	Plural Form		Rule	Plural Form
1. punch			10. way		
2. veto			11. shelf		
3. hero			12. gulf		
4. hole			13. series		
5. levy			14. tooth		
6. fox			15. day		
7. man			16. hobby		
8. salmon			17. foot		
9. earmuff			18. thief		

EDITING

Exercise 3: Punctuate the Kay and Robert story, "Brotherless." (Part 3 of 5)
Editing Guide: **End Marks: 6 Capitals: 16 Commas: 10 Quotation Marks: 8 Apostrophes: 1 Periods: 1**

kay robert said *brotherless* is not a correct word i think we should go ask ms wright she teaches advanced english and she would know as robert walked away he kept muttering to himself i know *brotherless* is not a correct word ill just prove it by looking it up in the dictionary

later as kay passed robert in the hallway she asked him sweetly well robert did you look up *brotherless* in the abridged or unabridged dictionary

On notebook paper, number 1–12. For each noun, write the rule number and the plural form that follows the rule. If a noun has two acceptable plural forms, use the plural spelling that can be verified by these rules.

RULES FOR MAKING REGULAR NOUNS PLURAL

Add -s to nouns without special endings.
1. most singular nouns.

Add -es to nouns with these special endings:
2. ***ch, sh, z, s, ss, x***.
3. a consonant plus ***o***.
4. a consonant plus ***y***, change **y** to **i** before adding **es**.
5. ***f*** or ***fe***, change **f** or **fe** to **v** before adding **es**.

Add -s to nouns with these special endings:
6. ***f*** or ***ff***.
7. a vowel plus ***o***.
8. a vowel plus ***y***.

RULES FOR MAKING IRREGULAR NOUNS PLURAL
9. Change the spelling completely for the plural form.
10. Spell the same for both the singular and plural form.

	Rule	Plural Form		Rule	Plural Form
1. lullaby			7. volcano		
2. video			8. shelf		
3. valley			9. goose		
4. belief			10. tax		
5. potato			11. elf		
6. pulley			12. child		

Home Connection

Family Activity for Vocabulary and Analogies

Divide into family teams. The first team will use vocabulary and analogy cards 29–32 to ask questions about the information on their cards. The second team will use vocabulary and analogy cards 33–36 to ask questions about the information on their cards.

Family Activity for Plurals of Nouns

Write the plurals of the nouns in the blanks. Then, circle them in the word search below. Words may appear across or down.

calf ____________
child ____________
church ____________
deer ____________
dog ____________
family ____________
fly ____________
potato ____________
radio ____________
roof ____________

Q E R H Y G H C P M S W A U V
W X F J A S D C O F G F L Y S
O R A D I O S H T U M P T E F
Z K M O Q D F U A T D E E R O
F U I G B X V R T J W Q A O T
P O L E L R E C O V Z C A O Q
L A I S U Y E H E Y C A L F S
T V E H F L I E S C G L J E Z
L O S F E N G S A U T V C S R
D B O T T E N U S T S E H I L
S R E O T A B R O O F S I M A
Z G C H I L D R E N H O L R P
E A R A S R A D I O E S D Y N
A D O G S T O R N G A T S O R

Puzzle Answers: calf/calves child/children church/churches deer/deer dog/dogs family/families fly/flies potato/potatoes radio/radios roof/roofs

Chapter 10 Checkup 48

Name:______________________________ Date:______________

GRAMMAR

Exercise 1: Classify each sentence.

1. __________ Take the overflowing trash from the birthday party to the incinerator.

2. __________ Were the potted plants in the sunroom watered today?

3. __________ Can you give me directions to the downtown conservatory?

SKILLS

Exercise 2: For each noun, write the rule number and the plural form that follows the rule. Some nouns have two acceptable plural forms, but you should use the plural spellings that can be verified by these rules.

RULES FOR MAKING REGULAR NOUNS PLURAL

Add -s to nouns without special endings.

1. most singular nouns.

Add -es to nouns with these special endings:

2. *ch, sh, z, s, ss, x.*
3. a consonant plus *o*.
4. a consonant plus *y*, change **y** to **i** before adding **es**.
5. *f* or *fe*, change **f** or **fe** to **v** before adding **es**.

Add -s to nouns with these special endings:

6. *f* or *ff*.
7. a vowel plus *o*.
8. a vowel plus *y*.

RULES FOR MAKING IRREGULAR NOUNS PLURAL

9. Change the spelling completely for the plural form.
10. Spell the same for both the singular and plural form.

	Rule	Plural Form		Rule	Plural Form
1. tragedy			10. class		
2. dinosaur			11. pulley		
3. roof			12. clock		
4. woman			13. video		
5. radio			14. foot		
6. series			15. tornado		
7. boundary			16. tax		
8. journey			17. half		
9. cliff			18. calf		

EDITING

Exercise 3: Punctuate the Kay and Robert story, "Brotherless." (Part 4 of 5)
Editing Guide: End Marks: 7 Capitals: 10 Commas: 5 Quotation Marks: 8 Apostrophes: 1

robert chuckled as he eyed his sister with respect kay ive decided to move on with my life he said besides i know that it is to your advantage to have a brother robert declared airily having a brother means that there are always boys around making goo-goo eyes at you

oh my have we increased our vocabulary since we discovered the dictionary retorted kay

Notes:

Chapter 10 Writing Evaluation Guide

Name:____ Date:____________________

ROUGH DRAFT CHECK

_______ 1. Did you write your rough draft in pencil?
_______ 2. Did you write the correct headings on the first seven lines of your paper?
_______ 3. Did you use extra wide margins and skip every other line?
_______ 4. Did you write a title at the end of your rough draft?
_______ 5. Did you place your edited rough draft in your Rough Draft folder?

REVISING CHECK

_______ 6. Did you identify the purpose, type of writing, and audience?
_______ 7. Did you check for a topic, topic sentence, and sentences supporting the topic?
_______ 8. Did you check sentences for the right order, and did you combine, rearrange, or delete sentences when necessary?
_______ 9. Did you check for a variety of simple, compound, and complex sentences?
_______ 10. Did you check for any left out, repeated, or unnecessary words?
_______ 11. Did you check for the best choice of words by replacing or deleting unclear words?
_______ 12. Did you check the content for interest and creativity?
_______ 13. Did you check the voice to make sure the writing says what you want it to say?

EDITING CHECK

_______ 14. Did you indent each paragraph?
_______ 15. Did you put an end mark at the end of every sentence?
_______ 16. Did you capitalize the first word of every sentence?
_______ 17. Did you check for all other capitalization mistakes?
_______ 18. Did you check for all punctuation mistakes? *(commas, periods, apostrophes, quotation marks, underlining)*
_______ 19. Did you check for misspelled words and for incorrect homonym choices?
_______ 20. Did you check for incorrect spellings of plural and possessive forms?
_______ 21. Did you check for correct construction and punctuation of your sentences?
_______ 22. Did you check for usage mistakes? *(subject/verb agreement, a/an choices, contractions, verb tenses, pronoun/antecedent agreement, pronoun cases, degrees of adjectives, double negatives, etc.)*
_______ 23. Did you put your revised and edited paper in the Rough Draft folder?

FINAL PAPER CHECK

_______ 24. Did you write the final paper in pencil?
_______ 25. Did you center the title on the top line and center your name under the title?
_______ 26. Did you skip a line before starting the writing assignment?
_______ 27. Did you single-space, use wide margins, and write the final paper neatly?
_______ 28. Did you staple your papers in this order: final paper on top, rough draft in the middle, and prewriting map on the bottom? Did you put them in the Final Paper folder?

Notes:

Classroom Practice 49

Name:______________________________ Date:______________

GRAMMAR

Exercise 1: Classify each sentence.

1. __________ The large stone in her ring is an expensive diamond.

2. __________ Tooth enamel is the hardest substance in the human body.

SKILLS

Exercise 2: For Part A, underline each noun to be made possessive. Write **S** for singular or **P** for plural, the rule number, and the possessive form. **For Part B**, write the singular possessive and plural possessive of each noun.

RULE 1: boy's	RULE 2: boys'	RULE 3: men's
For a singular noun — add ('s)	**For a plural noun that ends in s — add (')**	**For a plural noun that does not end in s — add ('s)**

Part A	S-P	Rule	Possessive Form	Part B	Singular Poss	Plural Poss
1. dog bone				10. boss		
2. children toys				11. man		
3. Smiths phones				12. giraffe		
4. monkeys food				13. mother		
5. Thomas foot				14. child		
6. agent badge				15. books		
7. Dennis letter				16. wife		
8. cats paws				17. son		
9. tractor tires				18. wolf		

EDITING

Exercise 3: Punctuate the Kay and Robert story, "Pass the Salt." (Part 1 of 5) **Editing Guide: End Marks: 8 Capitals: 13 Commas: 4 Quotation Marks: 4 Single Quotes: 2 Apostrophes: 1 Homonyms: 1**

the stillness at the table was electrifying brother and sister glared at each other as kay slowly repeated pass the salt i need the salt i dont care how you do it i just want you to pass the stupid salt

robert was going to do know such thing his mischievous eyes twinkled as he watched his serious-minded sister work herself up until she was boiling he replied sweetly you have to say i love you robert

Notes:

Classroom Practice 50

Name:______________________________ Date:______________

GRAMMAR

Exercise 1: Classify each sentence.

1. __________ In the evenings, my father is the manager at the theater in town.

2. __________ His speech was an informative message about the extinction of many species.

SKILLS

Exercise 2: For Part A, underline each noun to be made possessive. Write **S** for singular or **P** for plural, the rule number, and the possessive form. **For Part B**, write the singular possessive and plural possessive of each noun.

RULE 1: boy's	RULE 2: boys'	RULE 3: men's
For a singular noun — add ('s)	**For a plural noun that ends in s — add (')**	**For a plural noun that does not end in s — add ('s)**

Part A	S-P	Rule	Possessive Form	Part B	Singular Poss	Plural Poss
1. mayor agenda				10. wife		
2. Russ dad				11. eagle		
3. donkeys ears				12. turkey		
4. Joneses toys				13. louse		
5. computer virus				14. radio		
6. women forum				15. child		
7. farmers crops				16. calf		
8. river current				17. cloud		
9. men clothes				18. church		

Exercise 3: Identify the pronoun case by writing **S** for subjective or **O** for objective in the blank. Underline the correct pronoun in parentheses.

	1. Save a place for Dan and (I, me).		5. Can you go with Bill and (I, me)?
	2. The fishermen were Stan and (I, me).		6. (They, Them) are good scissors.
	3. Mom made Jon and (I, me) a cake.		7. (We, Us) girls couldn't see the kite.
	4. Dave and (he, him) mowed yards.		8. Buy a ticket from (we, us) girls.

EDITING

Exercise 4: Punctuate the Kay and Robert story, "Pass the Salt." (Part 2 of 5) **Editing Guide: End Marks: 8 Capitals: 14 Commas: 4 Quotation Marks: 4 Single Quotes: 2 Apostrophes: 2 Homonyms: 2 Periods: 1**

kay eyed her brother angrily this was going to far her voice snapped as she said you are really the pits who do you think you are mr big shot

im your brother im the one who has too pass the salt you are my sister you are the one who has to say i love you robert

Notes:

Classroom Practice 51

Name:______________________________ Date:______________

GRAMMAR

▶ **Exercise 1:** Classify each sentence.

1. ________ The flowerbed in my neighbor's yard is a beautiful arrangement of different blossoms.

2. ________ Life, liberty, and the pursuit of happiness are the foundations of our great nation.

SKILLS

▶ **Exercise 2: For Part A**, underline each noun to be made possessive. Write **S** for singular or **P** for plural, the rule number, and the possessive form. **For Part B**, write the singular possessive and plural possessive of each noun.

RULE 1: boy's	RULE 2: boys'	RULE 3: men's
For a singular noun — add ('s)	**For a plural noun that ends in s — add (')**	**For a plural noun that does not end in s — add ('s)**

Part A	S-P	Rule	Possessive Form	Part B	Singular Poss	Plural Poss
1. volcano steam				8. meteor		
2. parrots feet				9. child		
3. burglar wrists				10. loaf		
4. circle diameter				11. thief		
5. barbers chairs				12. turkey		
6. mice footprints				13. box		
7. Ross grandma				14. grass		

▶ **Exercise 3:** Identify the pronoun case by writing **S** for subjective or **O** for objective in the blank. Underline the correct pronoun in parentheses.

	1. (We, Us) boys heard a loud noise.		5. For (they, them), I will buy a ticket.
	2. Buy (he and I, him and me) a pizza.		6. (We, Us) voted for Joyce for president.
	3. He took (we, us) girls to a game.		7. Joan's mom saw (I, me) at the mall.
	4. Please loan (I, me) your keys.		8. My uncle's only child is (she, her).

EDITING

▶ **Exercise 4:** Punctuate the Kay and Robert story, "Pass the Salt." (Part 3 of 5) **Editing Guide: End Marks: 10 Capitals: 13 Commas: 6 Quotation Marks: 8 Apostrophes: 3 Misspelled Words: 1**

oh brother why do sisters have brothers i just dont understand you why are you making such a big issue out of such a little thing as passing the salt kay fumed as she watched the fun her brother was having then her anger faded and her eyes sparkled she stifled a gigle as she said i cant say it i just cant

sure you can said robert merrily take a deep breath and start with the word i

Notes:

Chapter 11 Checkup 52

Name:______________________________ Date:______________

GRAMMAR

Exercise 1: Classify each sentence.

1. __________ Today is the first anniversary of our company's grand opening.

2. __________ During the war, my sister was the first female pilot in the military.

3. __________ The mink is a slender, aggressive, water-loving member of the weasel family.

SKILLS

Exercise 2: For Part A, underline each noun to be made possessive. Write **S** for singular or **P** for plural, the rule number, and the possessive form. **For Part B**, write the singular possessive and plural possessive of each noun.

RULE 1: boy's	RULE 2: boys'	RULE 3: men's
For a singular noun — add ('s)	For a plural noun that ends in s — add (')	For a plural noun that does not end in s — add ('s)

Part A	S-P	Rule	Possessive Form	Part B	Singular Poss	Plural Poss
1. rabbit ears				9. shelf		
2. women hats				10. ox		
3. serpent venom				11. tomato		
4. widows sons				12. wolf		
5. Wes mentor				13. comb		
6. donkeys tails				14. child		
7. firemen boots				15. parent		
8. soldiers rifles				16. mouse		

Exercise 3: Identify the pronoun case by writing **S** for subjective or **O** for objective in the blank. Underline the correct pronoun in parentheses.

	1. I talked to (he, him) earlier today.		5. (He, Him) looked at a new truck today.
	2. Jo is going with (she, her) to the dance.		6. The attorney gave advice to (they, them).
	3. Yes, this is (she, her).		7. (We, Us) made oatmeal cookies yesterday.
	4. Most of the class voted for (he, him).		8. Aunt Sue bought (I, me) a new pair of shoes.

EDITING

Exercise 4: Punctuate the Kay and Robert story, "Pass the Salt." (Part 4 of 5) **Editing Guide: End Marks: 5 Capitals: 10 Commas: 5 Quotation Marks: 4 Apostrophes: 1 Homonyms: 1 Periods: 1 Misspelled Words: 1**

kay tossed her head and said airily why should i this hole conversation has goten out of hand ill just get the salt myself kay walked to the end of the table picked up the salt and turned to her brother i love you mr big shot she said sweetly

Notes:

Classroom Practice 53

Name:______________________________ Date:______________

INDEPENDENT PRACTICE & REVISED SENTENCES

1. **Write a Practice Sentence according to the labels you choose.**
   Use SN/SP LV PrN as your main labels. You may use the other labels in any order and as many times as you wish in order to make a Practice Sentence.
   Chapter 11 labels for a Practice Sentence: SN/SP, LV, PrN, Adj, Adv, A, P, OP, PPA, C, HV, I, PNA
2. **Write a Revised Sentence. Use the following revision strategies: *synonym (syn), antonym (ant), word change (wc), added word (add), deleted word (delete),* or *no change (nc)*. Under each word, write the abbreviation of the revision strategy you use.**

Labels:

Practice:

Revised:

Strategies:

Labels:

Practice:

Revised:

Strategies:

Labels:

Practice:

Revised:

Strategies:

Notes:

Chapter 11 Writing Evaluation Guide

Name:____ Date:_______________

ROUGH DRAFT CHECK

______ 1. Did you write your rough draft in pencil?
______ 2. Did you write the correct headings on the first seven lines of your paper?
______ 3. Did you use extra wide margins and skip every other line?
______ 4. Did you write a title at the end of your rough draft?
______ 5. Did you place your edited rough draft in your Rough Draft folder?

REVISING CHECK

______ 6. Did you identify the purpose, type of writing, and audience?
______ 7. Did you check for a topic, topic sentence, and sentences supporting the topic?
______ 8. Did you check sentences for the right order, and did you combine, rearrange, or delete sentences when necessary?
______ 9. Did you check for a variety of simple, compound, and complex sentences?
______ 10. Did you check for any left out, repeated, or unnecessary words?
______ 11. Did you check for the best choice of words by replacing or deleting unclear words?
______ 12. Did you check the content for interest and creativity?
______ 13. Did you check the voice to make sure the writing says what you want it to say?

EDITING CHECK

______ 14. Did you indent each paragraph?
______ 15. Did you put an end mark at the end of every sentence?
______ 16. Did you capitalize the first word of every sentence?
______ 17. Did you check for all other capitalization mistakes?
______ 18. Did you check for all punctuation mistakes? *(commas, periods, apostrophes, quotation marks, underlining)*
______ 19. Did you check for misspelled words and for incorrect homonym choices?
______ 20. Did you check for incorrect spellings of plural and possessive forms?
______ 21. Did you check for correct construction and punctuation of your sentences?
______ 22. Did you check for usage mistakes? *(subject/verb agreement, a/an choices, contractions, verb tenses, pronoun/antecedent agreement, pronoun cases, degrees of adjectives, double negatives, etc.)*
______ 23. Did you put your revised and edited paper in the Rough Draft folder?

FINAL PAPER CHECK

______ 24. Did you write the final paper in pencil?
______ 25. Did you center the title on the top line and center your name under the title?
______ 26. Did you skip a line before starting the writing assignment?
______ 27. Did you single-space, use wide margins, and write the final paper neatly?
______ 28. Did you staple your papers in this order: final paper on top, rough draft in the middle, and prewriting map on the bottom? Did you put them in the Final Paper folder?

Notes:

Classroom Practice 54

Name:____ Date:_______________

GRAMMAR

▶ **Exercise 1:** Classify each sentence.

1. __________ In December, my little brother was an angel in the play at school.

2. __________ Our parents gave my sister an expensive present for her college graduation.

3. __________ Yikes! Those gophers dug a maze of tunnels in Mr. Hoodwink's big hayfield!

4. __________ Give me the key to your car.

SKILLS

▶ **Exercise 2:** Complete the table. Then, underline the pronoun in parentheses that agrees with its antecedent.

Pronoun-Antecedent Agreement	Antecedent	S or P	Pronoun S or P
1. The winner of the scholarship is (I, me).			
2. The kittens played with (his, their) toys.			
3. The customer signed (his, their) name in ink.			
4. Cindy filled (her, their) grocery basket full.			
5. The calf jumped out of (its, their) stall.			
6. The janitor misplaced (his, their) mop.			
7. The men were in (his, their) meeting.			
8. She made dresses and sold (it, them).			

▶ **Exercise 3:** Write the letter of the word that best completes the analogy.

dentist : teeth :: mechanic : ____ a. wrench b. screwdriver c. garage d. engines

EDITING

▶ **Exercise 4:** Punctuate the Kay and Robert story, "The Cinnamon Rolls." (Part 1 of 5)
Editing Guide: End Marks: 5 Capitals: 9 Commas: 1 Quotation Marks: 8 Apostrophes: 3 Homonyms: 1

i cant believe you ate four cinnamon rolls during lunch exclaimed kay youre probably going to throw up during pe

i will not robert replied you are just mad because i wouldnt give you won of my cinnamon rolls

Notes:

Classroom Practice 55

Name:______________________________ Date:______________

GRAMMAR

▶ **Exercise 1:** Classify each sentence.

1. __________ The shade from the maple tree is a cool and welcome relief.

2. __________ Eventually, the fat, hairy caterpillars will turn into beautiful butterflies.

SKILLS

▶ **Exercise 2:** Complete the table. Then, underline the pronoun in parentheses that agrees with its antecedent.

Pronoun-Antecedent Agreement	Antecedent	S or P	Pronoun S or P
1. The nurses checked (her, their) patients.			
2. Dad had pie for (his, their) birthday treat.			
3. Everybody heard (his, their) own name called.			
4. Anyone can buy (his, their) own football jacket.			
5. Several ate (his, their) lunches in the park.			

▶ **Exercise 3:** Complete the table and underline the correct verb. **N/Pro** means to identify the subject as a noun or pronoun. Use **S** for singular and **P** for plural.

Subject-Verb Agreement	Subject	N/Pro	S or P	Verb S or P
1. Either of the two choices (is, are) fine.				
2. Two sacks of money (was, were) found today.				
3. A sack of money (was, were) found today.				
4. Everything (don't, doesn't) go up to the attic.				
5. All of the band members (feel, feels) proud.				

▶ **Exercise 4:** Identify these indefinite pronouns as singular (**S**), plural (**P**), or either (**E**) singular or plural.

1. ___ nobody 2. ___ some 3. ___ each 4. ___ few 5. ___ everyone

EDITING

▶ **Exercise 5:** Punctuate the Kay and Robert story, "The Cinnamon Rolls." (Part 2 of 5)
Editing Guide: End Marks: 6 Capitals: 7 Commas: 3 Quotation Marks: 4 Homonyms: 1 Misspelled Words: 2

kay was getting irritated you really have a lot of nerve she snapped you begged for my cinnamon roll until i gave it to you then you sweet-talked two more girls out of there cinnamon rolls that made three and your cinnamon roll made four the least you coud have done was to give my cinamon roll back to me

Notes:

Classroom Practice 56

Name:______________________________ Date:______________

GRAMMAR

▶ **Exercise 1:** Classify each sentence.

1. __________ Are the grapevines used for wreaths and decorations after the harvest?

2. __________ After the tornado, the retired electrician offered the people his services for a very small fee.

SKILLS

▶ **Exercise 2:** Complete the table. Then, underline the pronoun in parentheses that agrees with its antecedent.

Pronoun-Antecedent Agreement	Antecedent	S or P	Pronoun S or P
1. Everybody sits in (his, their) assigned seat.			
2. The acrobats stood on (his, their) heads.			
3. Many took cushions for (his, their) comfort.			
4. Somebody on our street sold (his, their) car.			
5. Everyone recognized (his, their) name.			

▶ **Exercise 3:** Complete the table and underline the correct verb. **N/Pro** means to identify the subject as a noun or pronoun. Use **S** for singular and **P** for plural.

Subject-Verb Agreement	Subject	N/Pro	S or P	Verb S or P
1. Some of the banks (was, were) closed.				
2. Nobody in our office (has, have) the flu.				
3. A bouquet of roses (grace, graces) our table.				
4. None of the winners (is, are) qualified.				
5. He and she (go, goes) swimming every day.				

▶ **Exercise 4:** Identify these indefinite pronouns as singular (**S**), plural (**P**), or either (**E**) singular or plural.

1. ____ any 2. ____ everything 3. ____ either 4. ____ someone 5. ____ both

EDITING

▶ **Exercise 5:** Punctuate the Kay and Robert story, "The Cinnamon Rolls." (Part 3 of 5) **Editing Guide: End Marks: 3 Capitals: 5 Commas: 2 Quotation Marks: 2 Apostrophes: 2 Homonyms: 1 Misspelled Words: 1**

robert tried not to smile as he said kay i had already eaten your cinamon roll and my cinnamon roll i just couldnt hand you won of the girls cinnamon rolls with them watching that would show lack of appreciation

Notes:

Chapter 12 Writing Evaluation Guide

Name:______________________________ Date:______________

ROUGH DRAFT CHECK

______ 1. Did you write your rough draft in pencil?
______ 2. Did you write the correct headings on the first seven lines of your paper?
______ 3. Did you use extra wide margins and skip every other line?
______ 4. Did you write a title at the end of your rough draft?
______ 5. Did you place your edited rough draft in your Rough Draft folder?

REVISING CHECK

______ 6. Did you identify the purpose, type of writing, and audience?
______ 7. Did you check for a topic, topic sentence, and sentences supporting the topic?
______ 8. Did you check sentences for the right order, and did you combine, rearrange, or delete sentences when necessary?
______ 9. Did you check for a variety of simple, compound, and complex sentences?
______ 10. Did you check for any left out, repeated, or unnecessary words?
______ 11. Did you check for the best choice of words by replacing or deleting unclear words?
______ 12. Did you check the content for interest and creativity?
______ 13. Did you check the voice to make sure the writing says what you want it to say?

EDITING CHECK

______ 14. Did you indent each paragraph?
______ 15. Did you put an end mark at the end of every sentence?
______ 16. Did you capitalize the first word of every sentence?
______ 17. Did you check for all other capitalization mistakes?
______ 18. Did you check for all punctuation mistakes? *(commas, periods, apostrophes, quotation marks, underlining)*
______ 19. Did you check for misspelled words and for incorrect homonym choices?
______ 20. Did you check for incorrect spellings of plural and possessive forms?
______ 21. Did you check for correct construction and punctuation of your sentences?
______ 22. Did you check for usage mistakes? *(subject/verb agreement, a/an choices, contractions, verb tenses, pronoun/antecedent agreement, pronoun cases, degrees of adjectives, double negatives, etc.)*
______ 23. Did you put your revised and edited paper in the Rough Draft folder?

FINAL PAPER CHECK

______ 24. Did you write the final paper in pencil?
______ 25. Did you center the title on the top line and center your name under the title?
______ 26. Did you skip a line before starting the writing assignment?
______ 27. Did you single-space, use wide margins, and write the final paper neatly?
______ 28. Did you staple your papers in this order: final paper on top, rough draft in the middle, and prewriting map on the bottom? Did you put them in the Final Paper folder?

Notes:

Classroom Practice 62

Name:______________________________ Date:______________

INDEPENDENT PRACTICE & REVISED SENTENCES

1. **Write a Practice Sentence according to the labels you choose.**
   Use SN/SP LV PA as your main labels. You may use the other labels in any order and as many times as you wish in order to make a Practice Sentence.
   Chapter 13 labels for a Practice Sentence: SN/SP, LV, PA, Adj, Adv, A, P, OP, PPA, C, HV, I, PNA
2. **Write a Revised Sentence. Use the following revision strategies: *synonym (syn), antonym (ant), word change (wc), added word (add), deleted word (delete),* or *no change (nc).* Under each word, write the abbreviation of the revision strategy you use.**

Labels: ______________________________

Practice: ______________________________

Revised: ______________________________

Strategies: ______________________________

Labels: ______________________________

Practice: ______________________________

Revised: ______________________________

Strategies: ______________________________

Labels: ______________________________

Practice: ______________________________

Revised: ______________________________

Strategies: ______________________________

Notes:

Homework 11

Complete the homework assignment on notebook paper. Choose one of the following writing prompts:

1. Write a friendly letter to the author of your favorite book.
2. Pretend you are writing a friendly letter to a pen pal in another country for the first time. You must tell your new pen pal some interesting things about yourself so that he or she can get to know you. Use a social studies book, the library, or the internet to help you pick the city and country where your imaginary friend lives.

Follow the friendly-letter form. Make up a reasonable name and address. You could research names from the country you choose. Even though this is a pretend pen pal, make sure you always use writing etiquette, or manners. This means you should not write anything that would embarrass your family, teacher, or school.

Note: For a letter-writing assignment in Lesson 6, you should bring an envelope from home. Also, bring the name and address of a friend or family member to whom you will write and mail your friendly letter.

Home Connection

Family Activity for the Friendly Letter

Glue the friendly letter below onto cardstock or construction paper. Cut the sections apart at the dotted l[illegible]s and glue or write the number and the title for each friendly-letter part on the back of the corresponding strip.

Divide into teams. Time each team as members put the pieces of the friendly-letter puzzle together a[illegible]entify each part. Check the correct answers with the number and title on the back of each piece. The team tha[illegible]co[illegible]pletes the puzzle correctly in the shortest time is the winner.

Friendly Letter

Titles: 1. Heading | 2. Greeting or Salutation | 3. Body | 4. Closing | 5. Sign[illegible]ure

109 Appalo[illegible]sa Tr[illegible]
Flagstaff[illegible]Z 00[illegible]8
April 12[illegible]0—

Dear Jenny,

My mom and dad surprised me with the prettiest pony f[illegible] ny [illegible]thday! He's brown with white spots. I named him Comet. When you visit next summer [illegible]e'[illegible] go on a trail ride near the Grand Canyon.

Your friend,

Alice

5. Signature — Alice
4. Closing — Your friend,
3. Body — My mom and dad surprised me with the prettiest pony [illegible] birthday! He's brown with white spots. I named him Comet. When you visit next summ[illegible] go on a trail ride near the Grand Canyon.
2. Greeting or Salutation — Dear Jenny,
1. Heading — 109 [illegible]sa Trail Fla[illegible] 00088 A[illegible]0—

Classroom Practice 67

Name:__________________________________ Date:________________

SKILLS

Use the letter parts below to fill in the blanks of the business letter.

TITLE PARTS of a Business Letter:

Closing **Signature** **Heading**
Salutation **Body** **Inside Address**

SAMPLE PARTS of a Business Letter:

Sincerely yours,

Ellen Warren

Mr. Frederick Rogers, Manager
Blue Thumb, Inc.
147 West Main Street
East Port, NC 00049

Dear Mr. Rogers:

307 Elm Street
Marshall, AR 00033

October 11, 20—

I would like to order twelve packages of Royal Blue tulip bulbs from your current catalog. Enclosed is my check for $38.95. Please ship the bulbs by UPS.

Business Letter

1. Title: __________

2. Title: __________

3. Title: __________

4. Title: __________

5. Title: __________

6. Title: __________

Notes:

Classroom Practice 68

Name:____ Date:________________

SKILLS AND EDITING

Write the capitalization and punctuation rule numbers for each correction in **bold type**.
Use References 11–13 on pages 13–16 to look up rule numbers. (Total rule numbers required: 42)

P.O. Box 94

Carlton **C**ity**, MT** 00017

January 18**,** 20—

Senator **L**arry **J. B**urns

978 **S**outh **A**venue

Lansing**, MI** 00029

Dear **S**enator **B**urns**:**

I want to express my support for your bill on energy conservation in **M**aryland**, M**ichigan**,** and **M**innesota**. T**hank you for all the progress you have made in these states**.**

Sincerely yours**,**

Jason **T. L**ong

Notes:

Homework 12

Complete this homework assignment on notebook paper.

Write, revise, and edit a business letter to the Chamber of Commerce in a city you would like to visit. Ask for brochures and information about hotels, restaurants, unique attractions, and local history. Also, use the Internet, library, or telephone directories to find information that would help you. When you get a response, bring the information you receive to school and share it with your teacher and classmates. Use References 194–198.

Note: You should bring an envelope from home for a business-letter assignment in Lesson 6.

Home Connection

Family Activity for the Business Letter

Glue the business letter below onto cardstock or construction paper. Cut the sections apart at the dotted lines and glue or write the number and the title for each business-letter part on the back of the corresponding strip.

Divide into teams. Time each team as members put the pieces of the business-letter puzzle together and identify each part. Check the correct answers with the number and title on the back of each piece. The team that completes the puzzle correctly in the shortest time is the winner.

Business Letter

Titles: 1. Heading | 2. Inside Address | 3. Salutation | 4. Body | 5. Closing | 6. Signature

14 Cliff Street
Salina, KS 00042
October 10, 20—

Salina City Council
102 Commerce Blvd.
Salina, KS 00042

Dear Council Members:

The lack of a traffic light or a stop sign at the corner of Cliff and Cook Streets has created a dangerous situation for both motorists and pedestrians. Within the past three months, nine accidents have occurred.

Since school children cross the street daily at this intersection on their way to and from Central Elementary, it is imperative that immediate action be taken to control traffic at this hazardous intersection.

Sincerely,

Peter Madison
Peter Madison

1. Heading
14 Cliff Street
Salina, KS 00042
October 10, 20—

2. Inside Address
Salina City Council
102 Commerce Blvd.
Salina, KS 00042

3. Salutation
Dear Council Members:

4. Body
The lack of a traffic light or a stop sign at the corner of Cliff and Cook Streets has created a dangerous situation for both motorists and pedestrians. Within the past three months, nine accidents have occurred.
Since school children cross the street daily at this intersection on their way to and from Central Elementary, it is imperative that immediate action be taken to control traffic at this hazardous intersection.

5. Closing
Sincerely,

6. Signature
Peter Madison
Peter Madison

Classroom Practice 69

Name:______________________________ Date:______________

SKILLS AND EDITING

Write the capitalization and punctuation corrections only.

Editing Guide: End Marks: 4 Capitals: 34 Commas: 6 Colons: 1 Underlining: 3 Periods: 2

203 shady lane
shady city ut 00606
july 3 20—

magazine clearing house
fifth and broadway streets
new york city ny 00721

dear sirs

your list of magazines is impressive i want to order house and garden popular mechanics and popular science send the bill to the above address i am happy to do business with your company

sincerely yours

j p jones

Notes:

Classroom Practice 74

Name:______________________________ Date:______________

SKILLS

▶ **Exercise 1:** Copy the notes below into an outline. Use the correct outline form. (The notes are in correct parallel form.)

NOTES:	OUTLINE:
Collecting shells	
Introduction	
searching for shells	
when to search	
what to take	
flashlight	
bag or bucket	
where to search	
clams in sand	
snails under rocks	
scallops in eelgrass	
cleaning shells	
boil for 5 to 10 minutes	
soak in alcohol	
pull out meat	
dry in sun	
displaying shells	
mounting	
labeling	
use scientific name	
tell where, when, and who found it	
Conclusion	

▶ **Exercise 2:** Place an **X** in front of those items that are parallel.

______ 1. wingless insects ______ 2. aquatic insects ______ 3. flying insects ______ 4. insects that bite

Notes:

Chapter 17 Writing Evaluation Guide

Name:____ Date:____________________

ROUGH DRAFT CHECK

_______ 1. Did you write your rough draft in pencil?
_______ 2. Did you write the correct headings on the first seven lines of your paper?
_______ 3. Did you use extra wide margins and skip every other line?
_______ 4. Did you write a title at the end of your rough draft?
_______ 5. Did you place your edited rough draft in your Rough Draft folder?

REVISING CHECK

_______ 6. Did you identify the purpose, type of writing, and audience?
_______ 7. Did you check for a topic, topic sentence, and sentences supporting the topic?
_______ 8. Did you check sentences for the right order, and did you combine, rearrange, or delete sentences when necessary?
_______ 9. Did you check for a variety of simple, compound, and complex sentences?
_______ 10. Did you check for any left out, repeated, or unnecessary words?
_______ 11. Did you check for the best choice of words by replacing or deleting unclear words?
_______ 12. Did you check the content for interest and creativity?
_______ 13. Did you check the voice to make sure the writing says what you want it to say?

EDITING CHECK

_______ 14. Did you indent each paragraph?
_______ 15. Did you put an end mark at the end of every sentence?
_______ 16. Did you capitalize the first word of every sentence?
_______ 17. Did you check for all other capitalization mistakes?
_______ 18. Did you check for all punctuation mistakes? *(commas, periods, apostrophes, quotation marks, underlining)*
_______ 19. Did you check for misspelled words and for incorrect homonym choices?
_______ 20. Did you check for incorrect spellings of plural and possessive forms?
_______ 21. Did you check for correct construction and punctuation of your sentences?
_______ 22. Did you check for usage mistakes? *(subject/verb agreement, a/an choices, contractions, verb tenses, pronoun/antecedent agreement, pronoun cases, degrees of adjectives, double negatives, etc.)*
_______ 23. Did you put your revised and edited paper in the Rough Draft folder?

FINAL PAPER CHECK

_______ 24. Did you write the final paper in pencil?
_______ 25. Did you center the title on the top line and center your name under the title?
_______ 26. Did you skip a line before starting the writing assignment?
_______ 27. Did you single-space, use wide margins, and write the final paper neatly?
_______ 28. Did you staple your papers in this order: final paper on top, rough draft in the middle, and prewriting map on the bottom? Did you put them in the Final Paper folder?

Notes: